**Royal College
of Physicians**

CW00970603

History and Heritage series

Re-framing disability:
portraits from the
Royal College of Physicians

Edited by Bridget Telfer, Emma Shepley and Carole Reeves

History and Heritage series Editorial Board

Dr Andrew Hilson (Harveian librarian), Professor Alastair Compston and Sir Christopher Booth. Commissioned by Bridget Telfer, project curator, Royal College of Physicians.

The Royal College of Physicians

The Royal College of Physicians is a registered charity that aims to ensure high quality care for patients by promoting the highest standards of medical practice. It provides and sets standards in clinical practice and education and training, conducts assessments and examinations, quality assures external audit programmes, supports doctors in their practice of medicine, and advises the government, public and the profession on healthcare issues.

Accessibility – wheelchair access

The Royal College of Physicians' 1960s Grade 1 listed building presents many access challenges. Extensive DDA work has been carried out since 2004, and the continuing improvement of our facilities and internal glass lift remains a priority. We welcome suggestions and comments from visitors to the building, and aim for the RCP to be as accessible as possible to all in future.

ISBN: 978-1-86016-415-6

Royal College of Physicians

11 St Andrews Place, Regent's Park, London NW1 4LE
www.rcplondon.ac.uk

Registered Charity No 210508

Designed and typeset by James Partridge, Publications Department, Royal College of Physicians.
Printed in Great Britain by The Charlesworth Group, Wakefield, West Yorkshire.

Contents

iv List of illustrations

vi Acknowledgements

viii Preface by Emma Shepley, curator and heritage manager, Royal College of Physicians

2 Medical or social? A note on models of disability by Julie Anderson, senior lecturer in the history of modern medicine, University of Kent

5 Realising 'Re-framing disability' by Bridget Telfer, project curator, Royal College of Physicians

10 Thinking about difference ... by Tony Heaton, chief executive of Shape

15 Public bodies: disability on display by Julie Anderson, senior lecturer in the history of modern medicine, University of Kent

35 Historical portraits of disabled people at the Royal College of Physicians by Carole Reeves, outreach historian, Wellcome Trust Centre for the History of Medicine, University College London; Julie Anderson, senior lecturer in the history of modern medicine, University of Kent; Bridget Telfer, project curator, Royal College of Physicians

81 Contemporary photographic portraits and autobiographies of disabled participants

113 References

List of illustrations

Historical portraits of disabled people at the Royal College of Physicians

27 Fig 1. *Mr Lambert* (Daniel Lambert), etching with stipple by unknown artist, 1809

30 Fig 2. Sara Baartman (or the Hottentot Venus), etching by W Wadd, date unknown

36 Fig 3. *Mr O'Brien, & Count Borunlaski* (Patrick O'Brien and Count Joseph Boruwlaski), etching by unknown artist, date unknown

39 Fig 4. *Théorie des ressemblances* (Chang and Eng Bunker), lithograph by C Motte, 1839

40 Fig 5. *Sarah Hawkes in her state of deformity*, stipple by unknown artist, 1836

42 Fig 6. *Sarah Hawkes as she at present appears*, stipple by unknown artist, 1836

42 Fig 7. *Master Joules and Miss Marianne Lewis*, stipple by Woolnoth, 1806

45 Fig 8. *The chinese giant, Chang, with his wife and attendant dwarf* (Chang Yu Sing), wood engraving by unknown artist, date unknown

46 Fig 9. Thomas Inglefield, etching by Samuel Ireland after Francis Grose, 1787

46 Fig 10. *Thomas Inglefield*, etching with stipple by unknown artist, 1804

49 Fig 11. *The wonderful spotted Indian*, John Boby, etching with engraving by unknown artist, 1803

50 Fig 12. *Magdalena Rudolfs Thuinbuj von Stockholm auss Gweden*, engraving with etching by Wolfgang Kilian, 1651

53 Fig 13. *J Worrenburg, the Swiss dwarf* (John Worrenburg), aquatint with etching by unknown artist, c1688

54 Fig 14. *Matthew Buckinger* [Matthew Buchinger], etching by R Grave, date unknown

54 Fig 15. Matthew Buchinger, etching with stipple after a self-portrait, 1724

57 Fig 16. *Mynheer Wybrand Lolkes, the celebrated man in miniature*, etching by Wilkes, 1822

58 Fig 17. *Israel, the twin brothers* (Lazarus and Joannes Baptista Colloredo), etching by unknown artist, 1634

58 Fig 18. *Lazarus Coloredo* (Lazarus and Joannes Baptista Colloredo), etching by unknown artist, 1645

61 Fig 19. *Mrs Everitt and her son, the gigantic infant* (Thomas Hills Everitt), etching with stipple by unknown artist, 1780

62 Fig 20. *Blind granny*, stipple by unknown artist, date unknown

65 Fig 21. *Joseph Clark*, etching by unknown artist, c1792

66 Fig 22. *The living heteradelph, or duplex boy*, lithograph by unknown artist, date unknown

69 Fig 23. *John Valerius*, etching by R Grave, 1698

71 Fig 24. *Mr Henry Blacker the British giant*, engraving with etching by unknown artist, date unknown

72 Fig 25. *James Poro* (James and Matthew Poro), stipple by Maddocks, date unknown

75 Fig 26. *J Kleyser* (Johann Kleyser), aquatint by unknown artist, c1718

76 Fig 27. *A dwarf* (believed to be Richard Gibson), oil painting by unknown artist (after Sir Peter Lely), 19th century

79 Fig 28. *The twin brothers*, aquatint by unknown artist, c1716

Contemporary photographic portraits of disabled participants

82 Debbie Allaire

83 Jamie Beddard

84 Margot Bristow

85 Hayley Davies

87 Tim Gebbels

88 Miro Griffiths

89 Colin Hambrook

90 Margaret Hughes

91 Christiana Joseph

92 Adam Lotun

93 Julie McNamara

94 Aidan Moesby

95 Mark Pampel

97 Saleem A Quadri

98 Penny Pepper

99 Patricia Place

100 Liz Porter

101 Julia Poser

102 Sophie Partridge

103 Mik Scarlet

104 Michael Shamash

105 Jane Stemp

106 Allan Sutherland

108 Karen Sutherland

109 Anya Ustaszewski

110 Phil Willan

111 Anna C Young

Acknowledgements

Bridget Telfer, project curator, Royal College of Physicians
The organisers of 'Re-framing disability' would like to thank all those individuals and institutions which have supported the project in a variety of ways: Vyki Sparkes, for her discovery of the prints and the initial idea; the Wellcome Trust People Awards, which was crucial in enabling the full scope of our plans to be realised; the Museums, Libraries and Archives Council (MLA) Documentation Improvement grant, which allowed original research to be completed on the historical prints; Julie Anderson (University of Kent) and Carole Reeves (Wellcome Trust Centre for the History of Medicine at University College London), for their invaluable research; Tony Heaton and Kate Larsen, from the disability-led arts organisation Shape, for providing guidance and expertise throughout the project; Geraldine McNamara, Laura Cream, Foteini Galanopoulou and other Shape staff, for their access advice and support; Ted Evans, Bim Ajadi, and Lynn Weddle for their artistic input and being a joy to work with; and Colin Lindley and Toby McNicol for their display work.

We would also like to thank the following for their advice on the project: Richard Sandell and Jocelyn Dodd, from the Research Centre for Museums and Galleries, University of Leicester; Katie Potter, Imperial War Museum; Sophie Weaver and Ciara Canning, Colchester and Ipswich Museum Service; Liz Taylor, Birmingham Museum and Art Gallery; Christopher Evans, Royal London Hospital; Jane Hughes, Royal College of Surgeons; David Turner, Swansea University; Anna Vass, Camden Arts Centre; Peter Herbert, St Pancras Hospital Conference Centre, Camden PCT; Katherine Mellor, Chelsea and Westminster Hospital; Stella Couloutbanis, Richard Attenborough Centre; Philippa Massey, Stamford Museum; Kylea Little, Tyne and Wear Archives and Museum; Jill Aeppli, DISC (Disability in Camden); Daniel Blackie and Anna Carden-Coyne, Disability History Group; Kate Horbury and Alexis Keir, Elfrida Rathbone Centre; Rosemary Howes and Michael Bond, Camden Physical Disabilities and Sensory Impairments Liaison Group; Guy Noble, University College London Hospital; Kim Morrissey, Euston Purple Poets; Amberley Hoydon and Jane Appleyard, London Deanery; William Schupbach, Wellcome Library; Samantha Prince and Laura Skorupa, British Polio Fellowship; Anne Vleugels, Birkbeck, University of London; Tom Shakespeare, World Health Organization; Chris Mellor, Piers Masterson, Frank Earley, Dave Eldridge at Camden Council; Matthew Black, Camden PCT; and Laura Pastorelli, Wellcome Images.

We would like to thank all of the participants of the focus groups for their hard work and enthusiasm: Debbie Allaire; Jamie Beddard; Margot Bristow; Hayley Davies; Tim Gebbels; Miro Griffiths; Colin Hambrook; Margaret Hughes; Christiana Joseph; Adam Lotun; Julie McNamara; Aidan Moesby; Mark Pampel; Sophie Partridge; Penny Pepper; Patricia Place; Liz Porter; Julia Poser; Saleem A Quadri; Mik Scarlet; Michael Shamash; Jane Stemp; Allan Sutherland; Karen Sutherland; Anya Ustaszewski; Phil Willan; Anna C Young. We also wish to thank Vishal Sharma and Thomas Wells for their participation in the project.

We would like to thank the volunteers on the project (Frances Jeens, Victoria Milvaques Siscar, Yewande Okuleye, Ashli Hibbitt, Kirsten Teasdale and Laura Fielder) and the staff at the RCP, including Tom Grinyer, Julie Beckwith, Andrew Hilson, Sarah Rogers, Peter Basham, Laura Sleath, Joao Baleia, Pamela Forde, Sarah Gillam, Holly Fenton, Suzanne Fuzzey, Paulo Nuno, James Partridge, Joanna Reid, Nicholas Ridgman, Linda Cuthbertson, Mike Finn, Glen Price, Clive Ostler, Stephanie Ellrott, Paul Young, Prakash Patel, Jonathan Messias, Andrew McCracken and David Sutherland. ■

Preface: Royal College of Physicians' print collection

Emma Shepley, curator and heritage manager, Royal College of Physicians

The Royal College of Physicians' (RCP) museum collections are the product of centuries of gift-giving by fellows. Oil portraits, silver and medical artefacts have been displayed and used at the RCP since its foundation in 1518. Active collecting was first noted in a 1596 statute stating that any member or noble person could have his portrait hung on payment of £10. Many of Britain's leading portrait artists are represented in the RCP collections, including Sir Godfrey Kneller, Sir Peter Lely, Cornelius Johnson, Sir Joshua Reynolds, Johan Zoffany, Sir Thomas Lawrence and Sir John Millais.

Works from these collections are prominently displayed today in the RCP's headquarters at Regent's Park. However, out of public view, the museum also holds a substantial, but little known, archive of prints and drawings in storage. This collection contains over 5,000 portraits of scientists and medical personalities, with representations ranging from Hippocrates and Aristotle, to 20th century practitioners. This comprehensive survey of the faces of the Western scientific elite dates from the 16th century onwards, and includes etchings by Rembrandt.

Given the RCP's long history of collecting oil portraits, it is interesting that the first significant gift of 'engraved portraits of medical and scientific men' was bequeathed only in 1891 by Dr James Butterworth Ditchfield, a relative of RCP fellow Dr Peter Roget (1779–1869), creator of the famous thesaurus. Print donations subsequently increased as fellows wanted to establish a comprehensive biographical research resource in the library and in 1934 Dr Thomas Hancock Arnold Chaplin FRCP (1864–1944), medical historian and print specialist, presented part of his own collection of prints in two oak chests, further enhancing the holdings.

A catalogue of the engraved portraits was published in 1952 by Arthur Harry Driver, but the print collection remained largely unexamined until 2005, when museum staff and volunteers began to re-catalogue. In 2007, the small group of prints that form the basis of our 2011 exhibition 'Re-framing disability' were brought to light. This fascinating lost group of 17th–19th century portraits show the faces and bodies, not of doctors and scientists, but of disabled men and women of all ages, walks of life and professions. Some, such as conjoined twins Chang and Eng Bunker (1811–74) (Fig 4, p39), are still well-known today and others, such as professional artist Thomas Inglefeld (b1769) (Figs 9 and 10, p46), born without legs or hands, are forgotten. We do not know when the prints came into the RCP collections or who donated them. Our records do not show them arriving as a group, so they are most likely to have arrived as part of other donated print collections, gathered by fellows with an interest in the field. They have never been researched or displayed since their arrival at the RCP, until now.

The significance of the prints, and the appropriateness of the RCP to explore their history, was immediately apparent, as was the decision that the resulting exhibition would not simply focus on the historical prints, but should be led by contemporary responses and insights from disabled people. One oil portrait and 28 prints were selected from the collection to be researched for the project, which drew upon recent work re-examining the hidden histories of disability in museum collections, notably the Research Centre for Museums and Galleries' (RCMG) 'Rethinking disability representation' project (2006–8). The story of the creation and realisation of the 'Re-framing disability' project is told by Bridget Telfer, RCP project curator, and by Tony Heaton from the disability-led arts organisation, Shape, in the following pages. This is followed by the research findings exploring the prints themselves and the autobiographical text of the 27 disabled participants involved in the project. ∎

Michael Shamash and Allan Sutherland,
focus group participants

'The social model empowered disabled people as it promoted awareness that society's negative attitude to disabled people needed to change.'

Medical or social?
A note on models of disability

Julie Anderson, senior lecturer in the history of modern medicine, University of Kent

Over the last 30 years theories have emerged that attempt to make sense of the ways that disability has been constructed and understood by society. In Britain two distinct models were constructed: the 'medical model' and the 'social model'. A number of further models for the study of disability have since been developed.

The Union of the Physically Impaired Against Segregation (UPIAS) was formed in the 1970s and was led by activists such as Paul Hunt and Vic Finkelstein. The aim of the group was the full integration of disabled people into society. Other groups, such as the Disability Alliance, which was established in 1974, focused more on the financial barriers disabled people faced. In the policy statements of the UPIAS, they did not use the terms 'medical' or 'social model'. However, the UPIAS is credited as being the inspiration for the social model of disability.

The social model calls for the rejection of the 'medical model'. But what is the medical model? Essentially, it is the dominance of medical approaches and of medical experts in disabled people's lives. The medical model is often symbolised by the International Classification of Impairments, Disabilities and Handicaps (ICIDH), which was developed in 1980. Essentially, this defines disability as a restriction or lack, resulting from impairment or disability that limits the fulfilment of a role considered 'normal'.

The social model defines disability as a problem with societal attitudes. Disabled people are excluded from society and isolated from it, are not allowed to fully take part in all aspects of social, working and cultural life. This model, which gained support throughout the 1980s, was very important as it concentrated on the removal of barriers to disabled people, whether physical, social or cultural. The social model empowered disabled people as it promoted awareness that society's negative attitude to disabled people needed to change.

The RCP's 'Re-framing disability' project is underpinned by the social model of disability, from the language used within the focus groups, to the content of interpretive material produced for the exhibition. ■

Further reading
Finkelstein V. Disability: a social challenge or an administrative responsibility. In: Swain J et al (eds), Disabling barriers, enabling environments. London: Sage, 1993.
Goffman E. Stigma: notes on the management of a spoiled identity. London: Harmondsworth Penguin, 1968.
Oliver M. Understanding disability: from theory to practice. Basingstoke: Macmillan, 1996.
Oliver M, Barnes C. Disabled people and social policy. Harlow: Longman, 1998.
Shakespeare T. Disability rights and wrongs. Abingdon: Routledge, 2007.
Zola IK. Healthism and disabling medicalisation. In: Illich I (ed), Disabling professions. London: Marion Boyars, 1977.

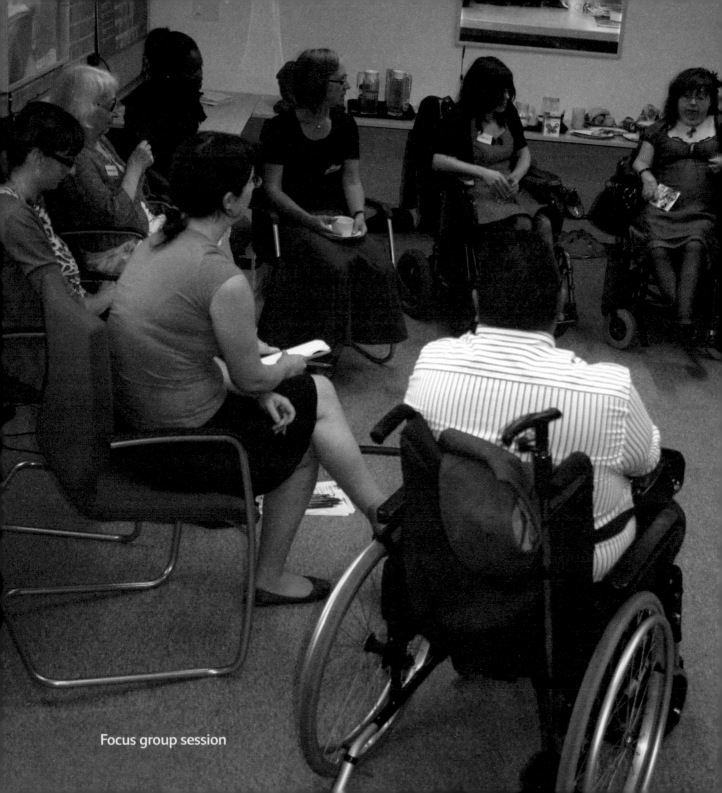

Focus group session

'Discussions were not just focused on the historical, as contemporary issues were also aired. Are there more images of disabled people around today? Are these images more positive? Do contemporary disabled people have more control over their lives?'

Realising 'Re-framing disability'

Bridget Telfer, project curator, Royal College of Physicians

Buried in the footnotes,[1] a report examining collections held within UK museums, revealed a wealth of material relating to the lives of disabled people. However, few museums display such items. Even when these objects are publicly exhibited, museums rarely acknowledge the link with disability, and even fewer museums consult disabled people when creating their displays. Why? A fear of creating offence is often stated. How should museums tackle the 'darker side' of disability history, the lack of agency, the sensationalism and suppression? Would exhibits inadvertently encourage audiences to stare in a way that was reminiscent of a freak show?

With these challenges in mind, we were attracted to the idea of exhibiting the RCP's historical images of disabled people – images that were often unique, artistically interesting, and had never been on public display before.

Initial talks and meetings with the Research Centre for Museums and Galleries (RCMG) at the University of Leicester and curators from the nine museums involved in their project 'Rethinking disability representation' (2006–8) cemented two points: the necessity of including disabled

'A third point made ... was that the social model of disability should underpin the project. This model rejects a medicalised definition of disability, and the need for 'cure' or treatment, and instead emphasises the need for society to change and remove the barriers restricting disabled people.'

people in all aspects of the project, and the importance of finding out about the lives of the historical people portrayed.

The first point was crucial for fostering a sense of ownership – this project was to be about disabled people's history and could not be curated solely by a non-disabled team. The second point was imperative for challenging negative stereotypes. Unearthing the lives of the people portrayed would allow them to be seen by visitors as parents, husbands, artists and professionals, and not be purely defined by their impairment. The project's research was conducted by Julie Anderson, senior lecturer in the history of medicine at the University of Kent and co-founder of the Disability History Group, and Carole Reeves, outreach historian for the Wellcome Trust Centre for the History of Medicine at University College London. Their combined fields of interest and expertise perfectly fitted the task, and their enthusiasm for the project was overwhelming.

A third point made by all those consulted was that the social model of disability should underpin the project. This model rejects a medicalised definition of disability, and the need for 'cure' or treatment, and instead emphasises the need for society to change and remove the barriers restricting disabled

Focus group session

people. This created a dilemma for us: how could the Royal College of Physicians as a medical institution host a project that rejected the very way the medical profession worked?

We approached Shape, the disability-led arts organisation in Kentish Town, London, and with the help of enthusiastic and creative thinkers, Tony Heaton, chief executive, and Kate Larsen, programme director, we made progress. The social model of disability could indeed inform the project, in the language and content of the interpretive material used for both the focus groups and exhibition. Indeed, some of the positive personal stories behind the historical images, of people as independent and in control, supported the social model way of thinking. However, a more nuanced approach would be needed when discussing the small minority of historical images that were medicalised: these would invariably bring up issues (often emotional) of treatment, cure and autonomy. Yet exploring disabled people's historical relationship with the medical profession, an element of disability history, was felt to be important, however difficult a subject. And what of disabled people's relationship with medicine today? To gather participants' views on this, we decided, could be a further positive outcome of the project: it would highlight the importance to medical professionals of maintaining an individual's dignity and self-respect.

A successful grant application to the Wellcome Trust (People Awards) allowed us to realise the full potential of the planned project, to include 27 disabled participants from across the UK in discussions centred on the historical images of disability and to provide access requirements, a fee for taking part and cover transport costs. The plan was also to create a legacy of contemporary positive portrayals of disabled people, images over which the participants had control. Ted Evans and Bim Ajadi, two Deaf film-makers, were recruited to create a documentary interviewing participants, while Lynn Weddle, a disabled photographer, was recruited to create their portraits. Participants were invited to personalise their image with props or costume, and Lynn used a shutter release cable, which gave control to the sitter: they could press the button and take their own photograph.

Stimulating discussions and debates ensued at the focus groups as disabled participants of diverse ages, ethnicities, backgrounds (including artists, actors, journalists and musicians) and localities (including Tyne and Wear, Merseyside, Chepstow and Edinburgh) came together. Themes of employment, autonomy, control and representation were aired as the lives of different historical disabled individuals were discussed and their portraits compared and contrasted, from the 17th century 'parasitic' twins 'Lazurus and Joannes Baptista Colloredo' to the 19th century Chinese 'giant', Chang Yu Sing. Discussions were not just focused on the historical, as contemporary issues were also aired. Are there more images of disabled people around today? Are these images more positive? Do contemporary disabled people have more control over their lives?

Participants were invited to further reflect on the lives of the historical individuals they had been introduced to and create a personal response in a medium of their choice. These ballads, poems and artistic responses can be viewed on the RCP website; www.rcplondon.ac.uk/heritage. One participant, Sophie Partridge (p102), a disabled actress and writer, created a blog:

'Somehow I had a sense of relief seeing these peeps, knowing generations had gone before, living in a world without any model of disability. Or even disability as a term of reference! As a young child, I knew I was never going to grow up a lot. But because I didn't know any small adults, I found it almost impossible to imagine myself in a future. Yet they were out there, I just had to keep living to find them.'

And it is the inclusion of disabled participants that is critical to the success of this exhibition. Only through their voices and views may we hope (in the words of one participant) 'to bring a humanistic view of disability to a wider audience' and encourage 'acceptance and celebration of difference'.

For the RCP, this project has been a steep learning curve. We are still working to improve access to the RCP's Grade 1 listed building near Regent's Park. We are still striving to change attitudes and ways of working, both internally and externally, to include and consult disabled people, to reduce the invisibility of disabled people in traditional museums, and to understand that disabled people's experiences, identities and views about how they want to be represented are all different. As one participant, Miro Griffiths (p88), said:

'For myself, I don't want to be known as Miro the person in the wheelchair, it's Miro with all the beliefs and faiths and values he has and oh by the way, he's also a wheelchair user.' ∎

'Good access to buildings ... public transport systems, accessible information, decent and appropriate services, education that meets our needs – removing the barriers to these "taken for granted" things will often be cure enough.'

Thinking about difference ...

Tony Heaton, chief executive of Shape

What's the difference between God and a doctor? God doesn't think he's a doctor.

It's a very old joke, but it always seems to surface in my consciousness when disability and the medical profession are mentioned in the same sentence. The relationship between disability and medicine is often contentious, and many disabled people are critical of the power the medical profession has over their lives.

Anecdotal stories abound. These are tempered by the huge impact that medicine and the medical profession has over all our lives. Many of us, including me, would not be alive without this intervention, yet others are impaired by it – a paradox of major proportions.

For those whose lives are untouched by disability and the barriers faced by disabled people, their families and associates, and who have little contact with the medical profession, there might be an assumption that our lives are inextricably linked to physicians, but for many disabled people this is simply not true.

Jane Stemp, focus group participant

Focus group sessions

We disabled people have illustrated, via the social model of disability, that often our cures do not need medical intervention. Good access to buildings and public transport systems, accessible information, decent and appropriate services, education that meets our needs – removing the barriers to these 'taken for granted' things will often be cure enough. These solutions are not the domain of the medical profession: they are potentially solvable by us all, particularly those of us who are providers of goods and services, or are in positions of power.

So, within this context, Shape was approached by the Royal College of Physicians. They have amongst their collection of objects and images depictions of disabled people from the 17th–19th centuries: could these portraits form the basis for something interesting, a starting point or catalyst to draw discussion and debate?

Should Shape be involved in a project like this, one with potentially negative connotations? As an organisation, we work within the social model of disability, believing that it is society that discriminate against disabled people, and we often contrast this with the medical model of disability, that sees disability as a personal tragedy. Would this collaboration between Shape and a medical institution

'Shape has been and remains a pioneering organisation, which, for the last 30 years, has worked with a plethora of organisations within the cultural sector, including the Royal Opera House, British Museum, the Tate and the National Theatre, training staff and advising on access.'

become a clash of ideologies? Would the images be medicalised? Would disabled people simply be seen as objects of scrutiny, gazed at through the microscope, labelled, named like some botanical specimen, defined in Latin?

Well of course we should be involved. Shape is a disability-led arts organisation working to improve access to culture for disabled people, if we are not prepared to enter into problematical areas or dialogue with unlikely partners, then what are we for? Shape has been and remains a pioneering organisation, which, for the last 30 years, has worked with a plethora of organisations within the cultural sector, including the Royal Opera House, British Museum, the Tate and the National Theatre, training staff and advising on access. We undertake a wide range of projects with a huge variety of partners and across all genres. In this instance we were fortunate to have Bridget Telfer as our connection to the RCP – she was open, honest, genuine and wanted to learn.

The proposition was stunningly simple: images of historical disabled people existed in the RCP collection, little was known about them, it would be interesting to commission some research and find out more about the lives and characters behind the images, and then to see the individuals within a wider historical framework, to get some sense of how disability was considered at that time. Following this research, disabled people involved in the arts and cultural sector would be invited to come together in a series of focus groups to have an open dialogue about the images and the research, and we would see what would unfold.

Shape's role was to advise on the planning of the focus groups, to host and facilitate them and also to provide disability equality training for all project partners. Shape also attracted disabled participants to the project through our newsletter and through follow-up discussions with interested parties to explain how the process would unfold. We also worked closely with Bridget and her team to formulate the content of the workshops. The RCP commissioned the academic input and research from Julie Anderson and Carol Reeves, who had knowledge and expertise in both disability and medicine, coupled with a great sense of humour.

Seeing the historical images for the first time was a revelation. Unexpectedly, most were images of people who did seem to have a degree of control over their lives, marketing their difference and capitalising from it. The majority were pre industrial revolution, the onset of the industrial revolution often being described as the time in history where the 'care and control' of disabled people began. Marginalised through mechanisation and standardisation, disabled people became 'misfits'. Yet the people in a number of these images were not subjected to that oppression; they had created a condition where they exploited their difference and controlled their own destiny.

This combination of people and subject set us up for a thought-provoking three days of focus groups and created sufficient material for the subsequent exhibition. It was an interesting partnership, and the work and commentary of the contemporary participants should speak for itself. And the voices of the long-past disabled people captured within these images, what of them? Well, much is conjecture. For me, the need to properly document our lives as disabled people, and to have this set within a contemporary context remains paramount. The need for a National Disability Arts Collection and Archive remains pressing, and the materials gathered from this venture between the RCP and Shape should become another important link in this largely hidden chain. ■

'Criticism has been levelled at the depiction of disabled people in the modern media, with accusations that images have frequently been limited to the sentimental, pathological and sensational ...'

Public bodies: disability on display

Julie Anderson, senior lecturer, history of modern medicine, University of Kent

Coaxed from the shadows: representations of disabled people

In early 2010, the international media published photographs depicting the world's tallest man, Sultan Kosan of Turkey, standing next to the world's shortest man, He Pingping from China. The discrepancy in their heights makes the smaller man look considerably smaller and the tall man appear much taller. This method has been used for centuries to accentuate size at both ends of the spectrum. In the late 18th century Patrick O'Brien (1760–1806), the Irish 'giant', and small man Count Joseph Boruwlaski (1739–1837) from Poland, were pictured together in a popular magazine (Fig 3, p36). Our interest in images of people with unusual bodies has long been a part of our culture.

Criticism has been levelled at the depiction of disabled people in the modern media, with accusations that images have frequently been limited to the sentimental, pathological and sensational, or that disabled individuals are simply not represented at all, despite the fact that there are more than 10 million people in the UK with a limiting long-term illness, impairment or disability.[2]

'Did people in other time periods look at disability or unusual bodies in different ways? Was this "way of seeing" more, or less, likely to marginalise disabled people? And finally, what resonance does this historical understanding have for disabled people today?'

There have been efforts to improve this marginalised view of disabled people by artists, activists and authorities. Disability has featured recently as a subject for artists such as Chris Rush, Doug Auld and Riva Lehrer. The sculpture of the pregnant artist Alison Lapper by Marc Quinn, which appeared on the fourth plinth in Trafalgar Square in 2005, undoubtedly raised awareness, even if some viewers were initially astonished. But disabled people are, for the most part, poorly represented in today's art and mass media, and often have little control over their image. These issues surrounding a lack of representation are long standing, as historical images of disabled people are also rare. Essentially, disabled people have to be coaxed from the margins of history.

The collection of portraits of disabled individuals held by the Royal College of Physicians (RCP) can be used to explore how disabled people were seen and understood historically. The range of unusual bodies and disabilities represented in the collection of portraits ranges from vitiligo, whereby the skin loses its pigment in specific locations, to conjoined twins, and date from the 17th to the 19th century. Some of the images depict very famous people who are still present in the public consciousness, such as Chang and Eng Bunker (1811–74), the first 'Siamese twins' (Fig 4, p39 and opposite), and Sara Baartman (1789–1815), who was exhibited under the name 'The Hottentot Venus' (Fig 2, p30).

Baartman did not, in fact, have what would be considered a disability, but her unusual body evoked great curiosity from medical practitioners and the general public. There are also a number of individuals who did not achieve fame or notoriety, but had their images memorialised nevertheless.

The questions posed by this historical collection of images still concern people who are interested in disability today. Who was the focus of these images and did the individuals have any control over their own representation? Why were the images created, who were they produced for and where did they appear? Then there are the wider issues and questions. Did people in other time periods look at disability or unusual bodies in different ways? Was this 'way of seeing' more, or less, likely to marginalise disabled people? And finally, what resonance does this historical understanding have for disabled people today?

Concepts and notions: changing ideas of disability

Between the 17th and 19th centuries, ideas about disability underwent significant change. In the early modern period (1500–1700), the belief that there was a correlation between sin and bodily deformity was well established, and there was also a strong connection between deformities of the body and

'COMPUTERS ARE
USELESS. THEY
CAN ONLY GIVE
YOU ANSWERS'.

Photographer Lynn Weddle and
Karen Sutherland, focus group participant

the mind. By the late 17th century, these notions were shifting and the increasing interest of medical practitioners ensured that disability, deformity and disfigurement began to be categorised, although there was little intervention, through a medical rather than a moral perspective. However, many disabled people lived within communities, and were not singled out for special attention.

As there was little medical intervention before the 19th century, images of the 'before and after treatment' that became more familiar in the 20th century, with the development of modern photography, were virtually unknown. The images in the RCP collection tend toward documenting unusual bodies, rather than pathologising them for the medical gaze. Exceptions to this in the collection are the images of Sarah Hawkes (b1817) (Figs 5 and 6 pp40, 42), whose 'cure' was effected by physician Edward Harrison (1766–1838). As a contrast to the 'victorious cure' through medical practice, an image from 1806 of the effects of cowpox vaccination to prevent smallpox depicts public resistance (Fig 7, p42). The portrait of a vaccinated boy and girl taking on the characteristics of cows reflected public anxieties surrounding the risk of degeneration associated with crossing of boundaries between humans and animals engendered by vaccination.

In addition, from the 19th century, with the growth of industrialisation, disabled people were excluded from the new modes of production,[3] and many were moved from mainstream society into institutions, often managed by doctors. Although this was motivated by a sense of social responsibility, its effect was to broaden the distance between disabled people and the rest of society. It is noteworthy that the term 'normal' was not commonly used in the English language until the 1840s.[4] Often excluded from mainstream employment, people with unusual bodies were likely to be compelled to exhibit themselves to earn a living. Advertising these individuals as attractions in large metropolitan centres such as London, Birmingham and Manchester generated large audiences.

Defining images: the RCP collection
The 17th–19th century portraits of disabled people in the RCP collection come from a variety of sources. In many cases they were produced in contemporary journals and widely read popular papers. Some of the images are taken from literature, and urged the public to come and view the individuals depicted, or from booklets given or sold to those who attended exhibitions. Others are taken from

presentations or treatises written by doctors explaining what they believe caused a particular condition, and using the disabled person as an example of the skill of their treatment. Still others come from autobiographical literature. In some cases, all that remained today was the portrait, and the person's story had to be constructed around what little information there was available.

Disability studies scholars such as Rosemarie Garland-Thomson have argued that creating portraits of disabled people confers importance on them and places them in a high status group, 'worthy of contemplation and commemoration'.[5] Many of the images in this collection do not follow the conventions of classic portraiture, and do not necessarily push their subjects into this realm of the elite. Nevertheless, the fact that individuals *were* depicted and their images published lends them certain significance. Not all of the images were attached to salacious stories about those with unusual bodies. Often they were published and re-published over many decades in journals appealing to people's interest including the *London Journal, All the Year Round* and the *Gentleman's Magazine*. They would often tell the life story of the individual, complete with physical descriptions or other facts considered interesting to readers. In the journal *Leisure Hour* of December 1865, the image of the giant Chang Yu Sing (1847–93) (Fig 8, p45) was accompanied by the following report:

'On entering the room one is immediately, as it were, transferred to a private house in China. Chang is seen at the end of the room, sitting like a joss stone upon a kind of throne, to which one ascends by a flight of carpet covered steps. He is dressed in the most lovely white satin garments, highly ornamented with beautiful devices wrought in needlework ... The whole party, both ladies and gentlemen, carry fans in their hands, and these they use incessantly, with a grace and elegance that I strongly advise any young lady given to flirting immediately to practise and adopt.'[6]

Stories would be re-told and images of the person re-published many times, as it seemed that readers of journals, particularly in the 19th century, had a great appetite for such historical anecdotes.

Fame or freakery?
Contemporary scholars have highlighted a long history of negative depictions of disabled people.[7] In film, television, newspapers and other media, disabled people have frequently been portrayed in

Focus group session

several traditional ways, which Rosemarie Garland-Thomson calls 'freak show ... charity ... or medical' genres.[8] Criticism has been levelled in particular at Hollywood films such as *Million dollar baby*, where permanent disability caused by injury is seen as the end of a productive life, and death is the preferable option. These popular images also serve to reinforce stereotypes of disabled people's lives as less useful and fulfilling than others.

The RCP portraits provide us with a glimpse into how people with different bodies were viewed, classified and lived their lives in past centuries. Perhaps surprisingly, many of the historical images conform to representational models promoted by disability activists today – for disabled individuals to be represented as active and independent. As with any historical document, questions arise as to their accuracy. There is little independent evidence to confirm what people really looked like.[9] The 'heaviest man that ever lived', Daniel Lambert (1770–1809) (Fig 1, p27) is the subject of many images,[10] and a formal portrait of him hangs in the Royal College of Surgeons at Lincoln's Inn Fields in London. However, the images of him differ significantly, so it is impossible to be completely sure. Artist Thomas Inglefield (b1769) appears in a number of images (Figs 9 and 10, p46), and looks different in all of them, but there is one common feature in images of Inglefield – the presence of drawing materials,

> 'The images can also tell us about the way that disabilities and unusual bodies were understood and explained by their contemporaries. A lack of understanding of certain conditions sometimes provoked wonder as people endeavoured to explain what caused them.'

identifying him as an illustrator who made his living writing and drawing. Indeed, many people in these portraits had multiple identities, not just as disabled people, but as workers and parents. These images allow us to see into their subjects' lives. In some, the casual nature and style of the pose and intimate details of the person's surroundings perhaps give us more insight into character than can a formal portrait.

The images can also tell us about the way that disabilities and unusual bodies were understood and explained by their contemporaries. A lack of understanding of certain conditions sometimes provoked wonder as people endeavoured to explain what caused them. The RCP print of John Boby (b1774) (Fig 11, p49), for example, is entitled *The wonderful spotted Indian*. The contemporary explanation that vitiligo was a result of the mixing of two races also demonstrated the fear that many Europeans had of racial difference.

Although the portraits are predominantly of men, there are a few notable depictions of women with unusual bodies. However, unlike many of the male portraits, women are not engaged in tasks or activities, and therefore would be less likely to have been perceived as workers as well as exhibitors.

The exception is the illustration of Magdalena Rudolfs Thuinbuj of *c*1651 (Fig 12, p50). Rudolfs Thuinbuj performs a range of household tasks and the image emphasises women's responsibility for domestic duties, but it also shows that a disabled woman is able to take on that role. We do not, however, know how much control Rudolfs Thuinbuj had over her own representation.

From 'pop-ups' to permanent exhibitions

In many cases, the reason these historical images exist is because the individuals exhibited themselves. Throughout history, exhibition was a common form of activity for disabled people, and was not always considered demeaning as it was a way to make a reasonably good living. London's Bartholomew Fair was a common place for exhibitors. Started in 1133, it had achieved international status by 1641, and many disabled people exhibited in the sideshows, along with acrobats and wild animal displays. The exhibition market was also fluid; people exhibited themselves and then retired, but went back if they needed more money to support themselves and their families.

Although fairs were good sources of income, they were seasonal, so during the year many exhibitors took rooms in pubs or private houses, and received viewing visitors at certain times of the day. John Worrenberg (1659–95) exhibited himself in the Plume of Feathers pub in Greenwich in the 17th century (Fig 13, p53), and Matthew Buchinger (1674–1740) (Figs 14 and 15, p54) chose the Two Blackamoors Heads in Holborn and the Corner House near Charing Cross.

The exhibition market was international and lucrative. Many of the people depicted in the images were from other countries in Europe, and would tour Britain. Indeed they travelled more widely than the majority of the world's population did at the time. Wybrand Lolkes (1730–1800) from Holland, gave up his trade as a jeweller in order to pursue a career exhibiting himself and earned enough money to support his wife and three children (Fig 16, p57). Lazarus and Joannes Baptista Colloredo (b1617) (Figs 17 and 18, p58), from Genoa, exhibited professionally throughout Europe from their teenage years, arriving in London in 1637 for an audience with King Charles I. Royal patronage could be an excellent route to riches and notoriety. Chang Yu Sing (1847–93) (Fig 8, p45) visited the Prince and Princess of Wales at their request, and as a souvenir of his visit wrote his name on the wall of the room in which he was received.

Unusual bodies could be temporary. Those who found themselves in possession of difference, even for a short time, could still exhibit for money. Baby Thomas Everitt's (b1779) career was likely to have been of short duration as he would probably have grown out of his unusually large infant body (Fig 19, p61). His mother took advantage of this 'window of opportunity' to transport him to London from Enfield in Middlesex for display to a curious public and thereby earn extra money for the household. Thomas Everitt died before reaching his second birthday, a common occurrence at that time.

Some people did not exhibit themselves professionally, but were enduring local objects of curiosity, for example 'Blind Granny' who lived in London in the early part of the 18th century (Fig 20, p62). She was said to have had mental health issues, as well as being blind in one eye, and was accepted by the local population as an eccentric living within their midst, despite the proximity of Bethlem Hospital (known as 'Bedlam'), an institution for people who were commonly known as 'lunatics'. Blind Granny was a feature of daily life and endured a type of affectionate notoriety, featuring in songs and verses of the day. Joseph Clark (d1650), also from London, enjoyed fame for his ability to contort his body and his face so extraordinarily that he could trick people into thinking they had met a different person entirely (Fig 21, p65). He would meet people and then return some moments later and beg from them as a disabled person. It was noted in the *Philosophical Transactions* in 1698 that the 'powers of his face [were] more extraordinary than the flexibility of his body'.[11]

The 19th century was a period of significant social change, and this was apparent in attitudes toward disabled people who exhibited themselves. In 1847, the word 'freak' took on its contemporary association with human anomaly, and 'freak shows', where groups of people showed themselves, rather than the individualised exhibitions of the 17th and 18th centuries, grew in popularity. Increasing commercialisation and commodification throughout the Victorian period saw the establishment of more permanent places of exhibition, rather than the 'pop-up' shows of the past. The wages were good, and people who exhibited themselves could command large fees. Many individuals negotiated their own contracts, kept regular hours and were not exploited by the more unscrupulous owners of exhibition venues. Some who had been 'managed' by middlemen gained independence, like Chang and Eng (1811–74), the Siamese twins, who sacked their agent when they turned 21, and controlled their own career (Fig 4, p39). Others, however, were controlled by their managers and found their lives limited and depressing.

The Victorians were fascinated by museums of anatomy and pathology, such as Dr Kahn's Museum in London, open from 1851 to 1873. Audiences were not limited to medical men, although some rooms containing specimens of venereal disease were off limits to women. There were a few living exhibits at Dr Kahn's Museum including the 'Heteradelph' or 'Duplex Boy' (b1857), who was shown a few times a day (Fig 22, p66). There is no information on where this young boy lived, or who looked after him. His family were in Lancashire and did not maintain contact. Sometimes disabled children were rejected by their families as the family may have been ostracised by neighbours or the community. There seemed to be no concern for his welfare from the men who came to see the boy. Women were banned from seeing him because of the centuries-old belief that attributed birth deformities to mothers being frightened by an unpleasant apparition during pregnancy, or even just viewing an unusual sight. The sight was believed to impress itself onto the developing fetus. Dr Kahn nevertheless dispelled this popular myth in his talk and pamphlet that accompanied viewings of the 'Duplex Boy'. Unlike some exhibitors in this period, we can be sure that the little boy did not have agency or choice about whether or not he exhibited his body.

Simply viewing a person with an unusual body was often not enough for the public, who demanded some form of entertainment to add to their visitor experience. In some cases, exhibitors performed feats of strength and agility. They also demonstrated how they managed daily chores. Given the public's perception of the limitation of their bodies, these routine tasks often appeared wondrous and amazing. John Valerius (b1667) (Fig 23, p69) who was born without arms, demonstrated his ability to fire a gun, shave and write with his toes for an admiring public. Others, such as Daniel Lambert (1770–1809), sat in a room and chatted to people who came to see his massive body (Fig 1, opposite). Lambert reportedly gave quick witted replies to those who teased him about his size, or asked him too many intimate questions. Exhibitors earned extra money selling items that they had produced, or images of themselves. John Valerius sold illustrations of himself performing his series of tasks. Miniature bibles were often sold by people of small stature and 'giants' were fond of selling rings demonstrating the circumference of their fingers.

26

MR LAMBERT.

Fig 1. Daniel Lambert (1770–1809)
Title on print: *Mr Lambert*
Etching with stipple by unknown artist, 1809
Size: 20.3 cm x 12.8 cm

Focus group session

**Fig 2. Sara Baartman
(or the Hottentot Venus) (1789–1815)**
Soft ground etching by W Wadd, date unkno
Size: 18.5 cm x 12 cm

Despite the relative freedom that exhibition provided for some of the people depicted in this collection, it was for many an unhappy and lonely existence. Such was the fascination for people who were different that they were often taken advantage of. Daniel Lambert (1770–1809) endured the indignity of being submitted to questions about his size, and his friends managed to weigh him without his consent by tricking him into getting into a carriage on scales (Fig 1, p27). Sara Baartman (1789–1815) was often poked with sticks and umbrellas when she was on display (Fig 2, opposite). 'Giant' Chang Yu Sing (1847–93) was not allowed to go out in public as his manager felt that it would mean fewer people would be prepared to pay to see him (Fig 8, p45).

Wanted: dead or alive

Although many disabled people in this collection of images controlled their own careers and lives, this agency did not always extend to them after they died. For some, exhibition did not end with their death. As Rosemarie Garland-Thomson reminds us, the 'freak's body is equally valuable, whether alive or dead'.[12] Some people with unusual bodies were dissected after their death, usually without their permission.

This was the fate of Sara Baartman (1789–1815) (Fig 2, opposite). Whilst exhibiting she had attempted to keep a semblance of dignity and would not be exhibited naked, even for the scientists who clamoured to see her body. It was not until she died and was dissected, without her consent, that scientists were able to confirm that she exhibited physical traits, including the enlarged labia, considered to be characteristic of female Hottentots.

People with unusual bodies were also at risk of their remains being displayed after their death. In particular, 'giants' feared that their skeletons would be placed on display as their unusualness was within their very bones, which did not decay like skin and fat.

There was a good reason for their fears. In 1783, anatomist John Hunter (1728–93) announced he would have the skeleton of the first Irish 'giant', Charles Byrne (1761–83) to display in his museum. Despite Byrne's express wish to the contrary, and efforts to ensure that Hunter was not able to gain

'... these historical images show that in other time periods, disabled people were represented multi-dimensionally, and that the emphasis was not simply on originality, uniqueness and the ability to perform but on pride, status, talent and entrepreneurial spirit.'

access to his remains, Hunter acquired Byrne's body by bribing his 'minders' while the latter was on his deathbed, and quickly boiled it down to the bones to avoid detection. Byrne's skeleton is on show at the Hunterian Museum at the Royal College of Surgeons, London, and still arouses debate today.

Byrne's fate led other giants to make even stricter provisions for their funerals. The second Irish 'giant', Patrick O'Brien (1760–1806), who also called himself Cotter, made elaborate preparations for his funeral, ensuring that his coffin bearers were teetotal and were not swayed to disobey his instructions by being offered alcohol (Fig 3, p36). In addition, he had earned enough money to be buried under a cathedral in Bristol so his coffin would not be at risk from grave robbers. Unfortunately for Cotter, some years later the floor of the cathedral was excavated and a curious public came to see his disinterred bones. Cotter's bones were re-examined in 1972 and it was confirmed that he was over eight feet tall.

There was also an endless fascination, not just with the death of unusual people, but with the process of dealing with their remains. When Daniel Lambert (1770–1809) died, people came from miles around to witness the removal of his body, the size of the coffin and the ingenious technological efforts that were undertaken to ensure that his large body was buried (Fig 1, p27).

The enduring power of difference

Although we may feel uncomfortable about the historical business of exhibition and especially the commodification of bodily difference, we have certainly not lost our appetite for unusual bodies. 'Freak' shows remained popular into the 20th century and our interest in difference continues today – the number of current television shows featuring unusual bodies, however sympathetically produced, are testament to the fact that we have not lost our fascination for looking at difference.

So can historical images tell a different story and show disabled people in other ways? While there is obvious truth that disabled people have been presented in stereotypical ways, these historical images show that in other time periods, disabled people were represented multi-dimensionally, and that the emphasis was not simply on originality, uniqueness and the ability to perform but on pride, status, talent and entrepreneurial spirit.

Many of the people in these images were trying to control the way that they were represented, in their clothing, their pose and their location. Similarly, disability activists today still strive for disabled people to control their own representations.

The evidence presented in this collection and the stories that the images tell, provide us with alternative views of disabled people. Overall, images such as the ones in the RCP collection are important for the study of disability history, as they provide us with more knowledge of disabled people's life experiences in different times and places. These images can give us a more nuanced glimpse into disabled people's lives. Many of the subjects of the RCP collection were celebrated, not pitied, for their ability to work with their bodies. They have been memorialised in images because they achieved a certain status through their lives, and disability was only part of their identity. They were often talented and active individuals who asserted varying levels of agency over their lives, were esteemed in their communities, enjoyed Europe-wide royal patronage, and remained in the public's memory and indeed their affection long after their deaths.

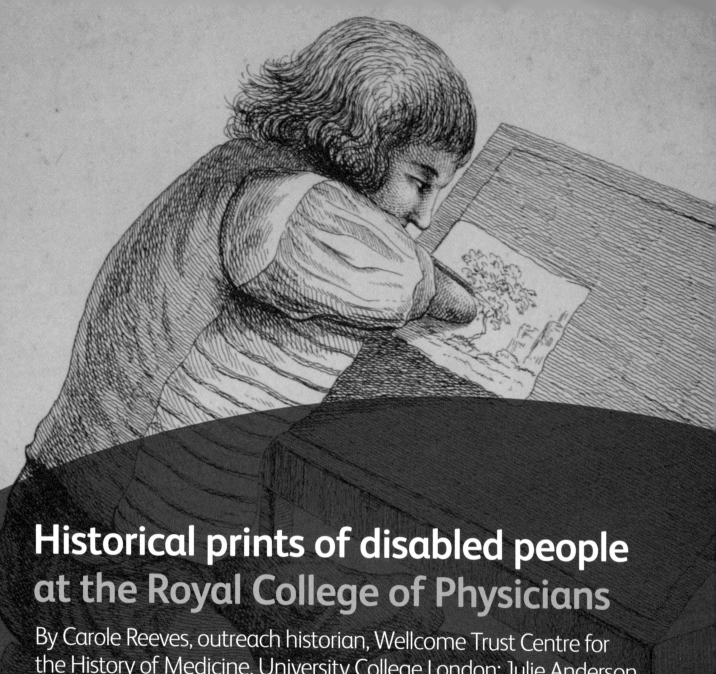

Historical prints of disabled people
at the Royal College of Physicians

By Carole Reeves, outreach historian, Wellcome Trust Centre for
the History of Medicine, University College London; Julie Anderson,
senior lecturer in the history of modern medicine, University of Kent;
and Bridget Telfer, RCP project curator

M.ͬ O'Brien, & Count Borunlaski.

Fig 3

Fig 3 (left). Patrick O'Brien (1760–1806) and Count Joseph Boruwlaski (1739–c1837)
Title on print: *Mr O'Brien, & Count Borunlaski*
Etching by unknown artist, date unknown
Size: 15 cm x 9 cm

'Giant' Patrick O'Brien (also known as 'Patrick Cotter') was born in Kinsale, Ireland, in 1760. He was 'discovered' by an agent in Ireland and brought to England to exhibit in 1782. Small man Joseph Boruwlaski was born in Poland in 1739. At nine years old, he was adopted by a local official and was later acquired by a Countess Humiecka. Boruwlaski was seen as a cultured gentleman and was a talented singer and musician, touring European courts. He came to London in the 1780s, where he continued to exhibit to the public.

Although O'Brien and Boruwlaski started their careers under management (in effect, they were the property of their agents), both eventually left ownership to manage themselves.

O'Brien was imprisoned for breach of contract after he objected to exhibiting without personal remuneration besides the food, clothing and lodging stipulated in his contract. He was rescued by a 'benevolent man' who proved the contract illegal[13] and thereafter O'Brien exhibited for his own profit and could earn £10 a day (£600 today).

Borulawski wrote his autobiography, *Memoirs of the celebrated dwarf, Joseph Boruwlaski: a Polish gentleman* (1788), published in English, French and German. In it, he defines himself by status, criticising those who identified him solely by his physicality as a freak or, worse, an eternal 'child'. He objected, as a 42-year-old, to being picked up and clasped to women's bosoms as if he was an infant.[14] Borulawski died in Durham aged 98 and is buried in Durham Cathedral, having previously expressed his wishes in verse: 'Poland was my cradle, England is my nest, Durham is my quiet place, where my weary bones will rest.'[15]

O'Brien was determined that his body would be buried, rather than end up in a museum like 'Irish giant' Charles Byrne (1761–83), whose body was taken by anatomist John Hunter (1728–93). When O'Brien died aged 46, his Bristol funeral was carefully scheduled for 6am to avoid crowds (unsuccessfully as 2,000 people attended) and his coffin was buried under 12 feet of rock in a church crypt.[16] However, when the foundations of the church were excavated in 1825, his coffin was opened and O'Brien's skeleton was publicly viewed.[17] ∎

Fig 4 (right). Chang and Eng Bunker (1811–74)
Title on print: *Théorie des ressemblances*
Lithograph by C Motte, 1839
Size: 25.8 cm x 24.6 cm
Published: Paris, 1831–44

Born in Siam (Thailand) 1811, Chang and Eng are the most famous conjoined twins in history, giving the term 'Siamese twins' to popular culture. They were joined at the chest by a four-inch tube of flesh, enabling them to walk side by side.[18] The twins were 'discovered' as children by a showman and travelled the world, arriving in London in 1829, where they exhibited at the Egyptian Hall, Piccadilly.[19]

This image appears in a French book *Théorie des ressemblances* 1831–44 by the Portuguese politician and naturalist José Joaquim Gama Machado (c1775–1861).[20] Machado moved to Paris in 1806 and is depicted within the print playing chess with Chang and Eng. He uses the twins to argue his '*théorie des ressemblances*': that the laws of similarities observed within animals can also apply to humans, and writes beneath the image:

'Their characters are similar; the two minds appear to be only one, as well as their wills. Several times I have played a chess game with them ... the calculation of the movements and the pieces, was almost the same every time. They would never talk to each other when they played. However, we should not be more surprised by the similarity of the characters than by seeing two widows (Brazilian birds) living in cages in two different places to lose their tails at the same day at the same time.' (English translation)

When Chang and Eng first went to France, they were banned from exhibiting for fear of harming pregnant women who, it was supposed, might be shocked into giving birth to a disabled child.[21] The idea, although largely discredited by the medical profession in the 19th century, still lingered in the public imagination.

By 1839, they had fired their agent and were successfully managing their own careers. They became US citizens, adopted the name 'Bunker' and purchased a farm in North Carolina.[22] They married two sisters who did not get along, so the twins divided their time between two houses and fathered 22 children between them.[23] They became very wealthy and were able to retire. However, they returned to exhibiting after their fortune was nearly lost during the American Civil War (1861–65)[24] – they were said to have supported opposite sides.

Chang and Eng died in 1874 after Chang, a heavy drinker, succumbed to a stroke. ∎

THÉORIE DES RESSEMBLANCES

Seconde Partie Page 84

Lith. de C.Motte

J'ai déja cité (dans ma planche des Tortues) les frères Faucher comme exemple; j'y en ajouterai encore un autre, celui des frères Siamois (adherens l'un à l'autre par le prolongement du sternum) qu'on voyait dernièrement à Paris, où j'ai eu occasion de les voir et de les observer. A l'exception de la taille, qui chez l'un a un pouce de moins que chez l'autre, leur ressemblance du reste est parfaite. Leurs corps présentent les mêmes formes, leurs visages les mêmes traits et la même couleur. Leurs caractères sont semblables. Les deux pensées paraissent n'en former qu'une seule, ainsi que leurs volontés. J'ai fait plusieurs fois avec eux une partie d'échecs, quoique jouant tous les deux ensemble contre moi, le calcul des mouvements des pièces était presque toujours le même. Ils ne se parlent jamais que quand ils jouent et seulement pour se conseiller. L'un n'a jamais vu dormir l'autre. Le principe des ressemblances n'ayant jamais été appliqué à l'espèce humaine par une fatalité inexplicable; ces Jumeaux ont fait une grande sensation à leur apparition en Europe, mais il ne faut pas plus s'étonner de l'identité de leurs caractères que de voir deux veuves (oiseaux du Brésil) vivant en cage dans des lieux distans l'un de l'autre, perdre leurs queues le même jour et à la même heure.

Fig 4

39

Within the illustration:

A *The Feet.*
B *The Umbilicus.*
C *The Left Arm.*
D *The Right Arm.*
E *The Ribs & Sternum raised.*
F *Great Trochanter of the right Thigh.*

G *The Knee.*
H *The Right Thigh.*
I *The Head fixed & inclining towards the left with the Chin resting upon the Top of the Sternum.*

Sarah Hawkes

in her State of Deformity

Joseph Robins, Bride Lane, London, 1836.

Fig

Fig 5 (above). Sarah Hawkes (b1817)
Title of print: *Sarah Hawkes in her state of deformity*
Stipple by unknown artist, 1836
Size: 19.4 cm x 13.5 cm
Published: Joseph Robins, London, 1836

Fig 6 (p42). Sarah Hawkes (b1817)
Title of print: *Sarah Hawkes as she at present appears*
Stipple by unknown artist, 1836
Size: 20 cm x 12.8 cm
Published: Joseph Robins, London, 1836

In 1831, the 14-year-old Sarah Hawkes exhibited herself in London, three years after she received a blow to the back of her neck which gradually caused her limbs to contract. Hawkes had been a servant in Dunmow, Essex, but, no longer able to earn her living, she came to London to exhibit.[25]

It is unlikely that Hawkes would have exhibited her naked body to the public and this image was created for medical readers. She was examined by many doctors, including the surgeon Astley Cooper (1768–1841), who treated her with contemporary 'cures' – bleeding, applying leeches, blistering and otherwise trying to drain off noxious humours.[26]

Hawkes had been in London a month when she was visited by Dr Edward Harrison (1766–1838), a Lancashire-born physician. Harrison began his treatment on 15 November 1831 and by 29 November 1832 Sarah was able to walk. In a letter to surgeon Sir Benjamin Collins Brodie in 1836, Harrison explained that he straightened Sarah's backbone by means of massage, splints, stretching and lying flat. No response from Hawkes' on her treatment is recorded.

Earlier versions of the portraits of Hawkes appear in Harrison's 1832 book: *The extraordinary case of Sarah Hawkes: one of extreme deformity cured by a method founded upon simple principles.*[27] Harrison recorded her treatment in detail, even noting her increase in appetite on 8 December 1831, when she consumed mutton chops for lunch, tea and toast in the afternoon, and sago or tapioca and white wine for dinner.

According to Harrison, the cause of Hawkes' deformity was a dislocation of the sixth cervical vertebra, causing paralysis and spasticity of her limbs through damage to the spinal cord.[28] In 1833, Sarah Hawkes was being treated again, this time by John B Serny who 'perceived that her deformity was returning, as one of her legs had become shorter by one inch, which had been occasioned by a fall in walking'.[29] After treatment, Serny reported that Hawkes was 'in good health, and able to walk several miles, and is not a little proud of her figure'.[30]

Harrison made plans for a spinal institute in London, and a public meeting to establish the institute with the donation of £1,000 from Harrison took place in 1834.[31] Harrison died in 1838 and his spinal institute in Stanhope Street seems to have subsequently closed despite his legacy of £3,000. ■

Fig 6

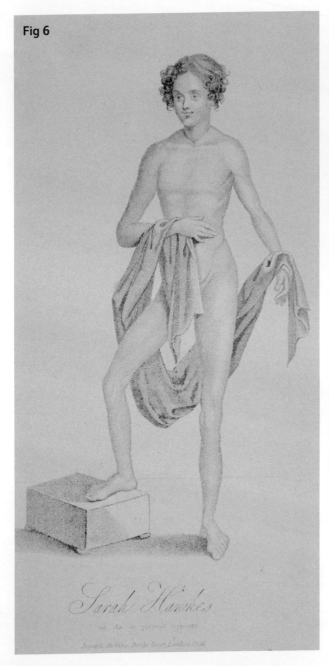

Sarah Hawkes

Joseph Robins, Bride Court, London 1806.

DIALOGUE.

ROWLEY. Admirable Prophet, See that terrible tumour in the Face, resembling an OX !!! dreadful to behold! (Rowley p. 43)

PROPHET MOSELEY. Visage of the boy in a state of transforming assuming that of a COW.!!! /p. 10)

ROWLEY. Another new disease from Cow-pox, the COW MANGE, a virgin covered all over with sores !!! a most disgusting Spectacle ! (p. 49)

PROPHET MOSELEY. Did I not foresee all this, nay more! But only part of my prophecy has as yet been fulfilled !! (Vide Note + p. 5 of Vindication)

Woolnoth del. et sculp.

Master Joules, the Cow-poxed, ox-cheek, young Gentleman___Rowley.

Miss Marianne Lewis, the Cow-poxed, Cow-manged young Lady ___Rowley.

Published by H. D. Symonds, Paternoster Row Feb? 26. 1806.

Fig 7

42

Fig 7 (left). Master Joules and Miss Marianne Lewis
Stipple by Woolnoth, 1806
Size: 19.5 cm x 12.5 cm
Published: HD Symonds, London,
28 February 1806

Vaccination has been a controversial subject in the UK since its original demonstration by Edward Jenner (1749–1823) in 1796. This image is one of many satirical cartoons from the early 19th century revealing the widespread public fear.

Smallpox caused thousands of deaths, blindness, deafness and severe disfigurement with pock-marked skin. It was the first disease to be controlled by vaccination after Jenner noted the common observation that milkmaids did not generally get smallpox. He theorised that they were protected by pus in the blisters received from cowpox (a disease similar to smallpox, but much less virulent). Jenner vaccinated an eight-year-old boy, James Phipps, with cowpox from milkmaid Sarah Holmes. James was then infected with smallpox and demonstrated immunity.[32] In 1792, Jenner published his work *An inquiry into the causes and effects of the variolae vaccinae*.[33]

Vaccination became compulsory throughout Britain during the 19th century, but there was resistance to compulsory health legislation and particularly vaccination. In Leicester, for example, the whole town quarantined itself and applied sanitary measures during smallpox outbreaks, rather than be vaccinated.

This print illustrates the popular theory that infecting people with cowpox would turn people into cows. It features two fictional children, Marianne Lewis (holding a toy cow) and Master Joules (leaning on a toy sword). Both have been transformed after having been vaccinated with cowpox. Marianne's skin has taken on the markings of a cow and she is apparently suffering from cow mange, as her body is covered in sores. Master Joules has developed an ox-cheek and ox-shaped eyes. ■

Fig 8 (right). Chang Yu Sing (1847–93)
Title on print: *The Chinese giant, Chang,*
with his wife and attendant dwarf
Wood engraving; unknown artist, date unknown
Size: 23.3 cm x 16.5 cm

This portrait of 'the Chinese giant' Chang Yu Sing (or Chang Woo Gow) is taken from a newspaper cutting *c*1865, introducing the reader to Chang, who claimed to be nearly eight feet tall:[34]

'The biggest, if not the greatest, man of our acquaintance is a young gentleman named Chang, nineteen years of age, born in the city of Fy-Chow, of highly respectable Chinese parentage, and lately arrived in London for the purpose of displaying his wonderful stature to us little people ... He is accompanied by his wife, whose name King-Foo signifies the Fair Lily and ... a dwarf called Chung who stands but 3 feet high ... attends the giant and enhances the exhibition of his size by contrast.'

A poster in the Wellcome's ephemera collection advertises Chang as the 'magic giant' at the old Egyptian Hall in Piccadilly, where he could be viewed daily (admission fee of half a crown for a front seat or one shilling for a back seat). 'Mr Siddons' would educate viewers with a lecture on China and Chinese giants, followed by the playing of polka music during which Chang would shake hands with the audience. The exhibition would be rounded off with a reading of Chang's *Ode on the Crystal Palace* and the grand finale – a dance by Chang's wife. The poster includes his address to the audience:

'I shall not attempt to express in words my gratitude for the reception you have given me here tonight, on this my first appearance upon a public platform in the western country. That you approach me with kindliness, and I am told, speak with a kind of admiration of the more than ordinary development of my body.'[35]

Chang's perceived exoticism drew crowds to view the spectacle of a 'giant' dressed in jewels, gold, embroidered silk and panther skin. Following tours of Europe and America, Chang retired to Bournemouth in 1890 with his English second wife, hoping that the sea air would cure his suspected tuberculosis. They made a modest income with an oriental bazaar and tearooms until his death in 1893. ∎

Fig 8

THE CHINESE GIANT, CHANG, WITH HIS WIFE AND ATTENDANT DWARF.

Fig 9

THOMAS INGLEFIELD.

at the Age of 20, from an Original Drawing.

Born without Arms or Legs Dec.r 12. 1769.

Pub.d Dec.r 22 1804 for R.S. Kirby 11 London House Yard.

Fig 10

Thomas Inglefield (b1769)

Fig 9 (far left). Untitled
Etching by Samuel Ireland after Francis Grose, 1787
Size: 27.7 cm x 19.1 cm
Published: T Inglefield, London, 28 May 1787

Fig 10 (left). Title on print: *Thomas Inglefield*
Etching with stipple, by unknown artist, 1804
Size: 17 cm x 11.6 cm
Published: RS Kirby, London, 22 Dec 1804

These two portraits of Thomas Inglefield depict him as an artist, sat at his work table with his drawing materials around him. A further portrait of him from 1787 is etched by Inglefield himself, and is important as the subject plays a part in depicting his own disability. The caption included in this portrait states that:

'... this extraordinary young man was born Decr. 18. 1769, at Hook, in Hampshire, without arms or legs, as here delineated, occasioned as his mother supposes by a fright she suffered when pregnant with him.'[36]

'Maternal imagination' was then a commonly held explanation for disability – a pregnant woman seeing a shocking or disturbing sight may give birth to a disabled child.

Inglefield was an accomplished artist and engraver. The caption continues to elucidate:

'... he has by industry acquired the arts of writing and drawing, holding his pencil between the stump of his left arm and his cheek & guiding it with the muscles of his mouth.'[37]

Like many people exhibiting themselves in the 18th century, Inglefield showed himself privately – in rooms at 8, Chapel Street, off Tottenham Court Road, London, 'where ladies & gentlemen may see him & many more of his performances'.[38] These prints would have been sold on the premises where he demonstrated his artistic skills to the public. Many people, including members of the Royal Society, collected disabled people's work for their private collections.

In Fig 9 we see Inglefield aged 18 working busily. In Fig 10 Inglefield is now aged 20 (according to the caption), in a rather more posed stance, dressed in what were probably his best clothes. Inglefield's clothes would have been specially tailored for his body, but this was the norm in the 18th century. 'Off the peg' clothing was then a rarity. These portraits of Inglefield as creator and artist clearly demonstrate that he is a working man, not solely an exhibit, earning his living by writing, drawing and etching. ∎

Fig 11 (right). John Boby (b1774)
Title on print: *The wonderful spotted Indian, John Boby*
Etching with engraving by unknown artist, 1803
Size: 19.1 cm x 11.1 cm
Published: Alex Hogg, London, 1 Oct 1803

John Boby (or 'Bobey') was born in 1774 near Kingston, Jamaica, to black slaves who already had four children. His mother, apparently, was so frightened when she saw her baby, who had white patches on his skin, that she refused to suckle him.[39] It is likely that she was terrified of being accused of adultery with a white man – plantation owners and white workers were notorious for violating female slaves.

The boy was sent to Liverpool at the age of 12 and christened John Primrose Richardson Boby. At some stage he was bought and exhibited by a showman named Clark and in 1795 was on display at London's famous Bartholomew Fair.[40] The image caption tells the viewer that Boby 'exhibits himself in different parts of England and Scotland'.

He also came to the attention of Johann Friedrich Blumenbach (1752–1840), the famous German naturalist who wrote about race and degeneration.[41] Black races were considered inferior to white races and the presence of white skin on black people created fear about the mixing of different racial groups. Such skin conditions, however, were also considered a 'quirk of nature' invoking a sense of awe and fascination within the public,[42] hence the title of this print, *The wonderful spotted Indian*.

Boby had vitiligo, whereby the skin loses its pigment in random patches. Although vitiligo can affect all populations it is much more noticeable in black skins,[43] and in Boby's time people with vitiligo were often called 'pied-blacks'.[44, 45]

The portrait shows Boby at 29 years old, wearing a dramatic costume, suggesting that these were 'show clothes' to be worn for exhibition purposes. In his left hand he holds a medallion (or perhaps a watch) threaded on a ribbon. His closely curled hair is black with a white streak running through the centre (known as a 'blaze'[46]), which continues onto his forehead.

Boby's life appears to have turned out happily – he gained his freedom and married an English woman.[47] ∎

The
WONDERFUL SPOTTED INDIAN,
John Boby.
Born at Kingston in Jamaica, & who exhibits himself in different parts of England & Scotland.
Pub.d by Alex. Hogg, 16 Paternoster row, Oct. 1.1803.

Fig 11

Fig 12

Fig 12 (left). Magdalena Rudolfs Thuinbuj (born *c*1612)

Title on print: *Magdalena Rudolfs Thuinbuj von Stockholm auss Gweden*
Engraving with etching by Wolfgang Kilian, 1651
Size: 29 cm x 16.4 cm

Magdalena Rudolfs Thuinbuj was born around 1612 in Stockholm, Sweden. In this portrait, dated 1651, she is 39 years old and is shown performing tasks of varying complexity, with her feet.

Rudolfs Thuinbuj is well dressed in the Scandinavian Protestant style, with lace-edged garments, including a deep collar, cap and apron, which is decorative rather than functional. In the central portrait she is shown firing a pistol and we might consider why this particular image was chosen as the main representation. Perhaps it was considered to be the most complex of her many abilities or maybe it was used to issue a warning – 'I may have a disability but don't mess with me'. The print contains a verse written in German:

'Because I, at God's mercy,
Have neither hand, finger or arm,
And therefore I have to help myself,
I do all this with my foot.' (English translation)

However, we do not know if Rudolfs Thuinbuj wrote this.

The small images within the print depict the following: unlocking a chest with a key (people at this period stored linen, clothing, etc in chests); threading a needle; stitching; knitting; embroidery; darning (?); lace-making or wiping (?); combing her hair; cutting with a knife; eating; pouring; drinking; cutting with scissors; wiping her face; blowing her nose; playing with dice or cards; eating with a spoon; wrapping up her child; breast-feeding a child (this would have satisfied the curiosity of viewers as to her ability to perform the role of mother and sexual partner); loading a pistol; feeding a child.

It is not known whether Rudolfs Thuinbuj exhibited or whether her abilities made her so famous that she was sought out and recorded by the German artist, Wolfgang Kilian (1581–1662). ∎

Fig 13 (right). John Worrenburg (1659–95)
Title on print: *J Worrenburg. The Swiss dwarf*
Aquatint with etching by unknown artist, *c*1688
Size: 10 cm x 5.4 cm

John Worrenburg was born in Harlshomen, Switzerland, in 1659. He was about 2 foot 7 inches (79 cm) in height,[48] and said to be 'as stout and strong as a full-grown man'.[49] It is not known whether he exhibited himself in Europe, but he arrived in London around 1688, when this portrait was created.[50]

Worrenburg was received at the court of James II, in Whitehall, where he met, and perhaps entertained, the king and members of the royal family.[51] Later that year (1688), James II was deposed and replaced by his nephew, William of Orange, who ruled jointly with James' daughter, Mary. Worrenburg's clothing depicts the ornate fashion favoured by the Catholic James II, whereas another portrait (in the Wellcome Library, London) shows a more sombre-suited gentleman in the dress favoured by the Protestant William of Orange. This suggests that entertainers and those who put themselves up for public exhibit found it politically advantageous to adopt the court fashions of the day. In the 17th century, it was the court that set the fashion agenda for the nation.

Worrenburg wears a sword and leans on a walking stick. Both were fashion accessories, although in his case the stick may have been more than a prop and could have been a walking aid for a man whose stride was much reduced compared with taller adults.

Worrenburg was well educated, multi-lingual, and sang for audiences who came to see him in his rooms at the Plume of Feathers, a public house in Greenwich, where he exhibited from 1691, and which still stands.[52]

In 1695 this dapper, talented man came to an untimely end at the age of 36, when landing at the port of Rotterdam, Holland. As he was too small to jump from the ship to the quay, he was always carried to safety in a box. On this occasion, the plank to the quay broke and Worrenburg was drowned in the box.[53] ■

J. WORRENBURG.

The Swiss Dwarf.

Fig 13

MATTHEW BUCKINGER.

Fig 14

Fig 15

Matthew Buchinger (b1674)
Fig 14 (far left). Title on print: *Matthew Buckinger*
Etching by R Grave, date unknown
Size: 22.9 cm x 15.9 cm

Fig 15 (main left). Etching with stipple after a
self-portrait by Matthew Buchinger, 1724
Published: Isaac Herbert
Size: 36.4 cm x 25.5 cm

Matthew Buchinger was born in Anspach,
Germany, in 1674, the youngest of nine children.
In the caption on Fig 15 he describes himself as
a 'wonderful little man of but 29 inches high,
born without hands, feet or thighs'. Buchinger
migrated to England in the early 18th century
and exhibited in London at the Two Blackamoors
Heads in Holborn and the Corner House, near
Charing Cross.[54] Admission cost one shilling for a
front seat or sixpence for a back seat, attracting a
well-heeled audience.

A man of many talents, Buchinger played musical
instruments such as bagpipes, dulcimer and
trumpet, performed conjuring tricks, played skittles
and nine pins, fired a pistol, danced a hornpipe
in Highland dress, and was a celebrated artist.
Examples of his penmanship are in the Harleian
Collection of manuscripts at the British Library.[55]

The RCP holds two portraits of Buchinger and a
notice written by himself dated 1837, advertising
his performance of 'miraculous actions as none
else can do with hands and feet'. Fig 14 shows
a young Buchinger seated in front of his drum
and quill. The self-portrait of 1724 (Fig 16) shows
the 50-year-old artist seated on an embroidered
and tasselled cushion. The curls of his wig
are composed of the lettering of six Biblical
psalms and the Lord's Prayer. The portrait was
commissioned by the publisher Isaac Herbert for
which he paid Buchinger 50 guineas – equivalent
to over £3,000 today. Buchinger sold prints to his
paying public.[56]

Buchinger was married four times and had 11
children.[57] Like many of the disabled people
represented in these images, he travelled more
widely than most people did at that time.

An elegy from a Dublin writer reveals the affection
in which Buchinger was held during his lifetime:

'Poor Buchinger is dead and gone,
A lifeless trunk who was a living one;
Trunk did I say, wherein all Virtues met?
I shou'd ha' call'd him a rich cabinet.'[58] ■

Fig 16 (right). Wybrand Lolkes (1730–1800)
Title on print: *Mynheer Wybrand Lolkes, the celebrated man in miniature*
Etching by Wilkes, 1822
Size: 25.3 cm x 21 cm
Published: C Johnson, for *Wonderful Magazine*

Wybrand Lolkes was born in Jelst, Holland, in 1730. He was apprenticed to a watchmaker in Amsterdam and became a skilful jeweller, establishing his own business in Rotterdam. When this did not go well he began exhibiting himself at fairs throughout Holland to support his family. At a height of 25½ inches (65 cm), Lolkes was one of the smallest men ever to exhibit.[59] Arriving at Harwich in 1790, he was received by a crowd of curious people. His first public appearance was at an amphitheatre near Westminster Bridge on Easter Monday.[60]

The engraving depicts 60-year-old Lolkes wearing a three-piece suit with cravat, stockings and buckled shoes. His apparel would have been specially made for him, but this was the norm in the 18th century, as high street shops were still a novelty and most working class and lower middle class households made their own clothing. Lolkes is accompanied by his neatly dressed wife whose only jewellery consists of a bead necklace and earrings, which may have been made by her husband.

Despite his age, Lolkes was reported to be very strong and active. He would jump around and stand on his head for an audience and spring from the floor onto a chair.[61] The image caption states that Lolkes had three children by his wife (this would have satisfied the sexual curiosity of readers), and that they were all 'live born and christened'. This told readers that the offspring were vigorous. In 1790 one in five babies died within the first year of life.

The image appeared in *Wonderful Magazine*. Magazines of this sort were expensive for ordinary people (many of whom were illiterate anyway), but pictures might be torn out and stuck up in coffee shops and taverns, or perhaps published separately as handbills or advertising sheets.

Lolkes made a very good living on the exhibition circuit and returned to Holland where he died in 1800.[62] ■

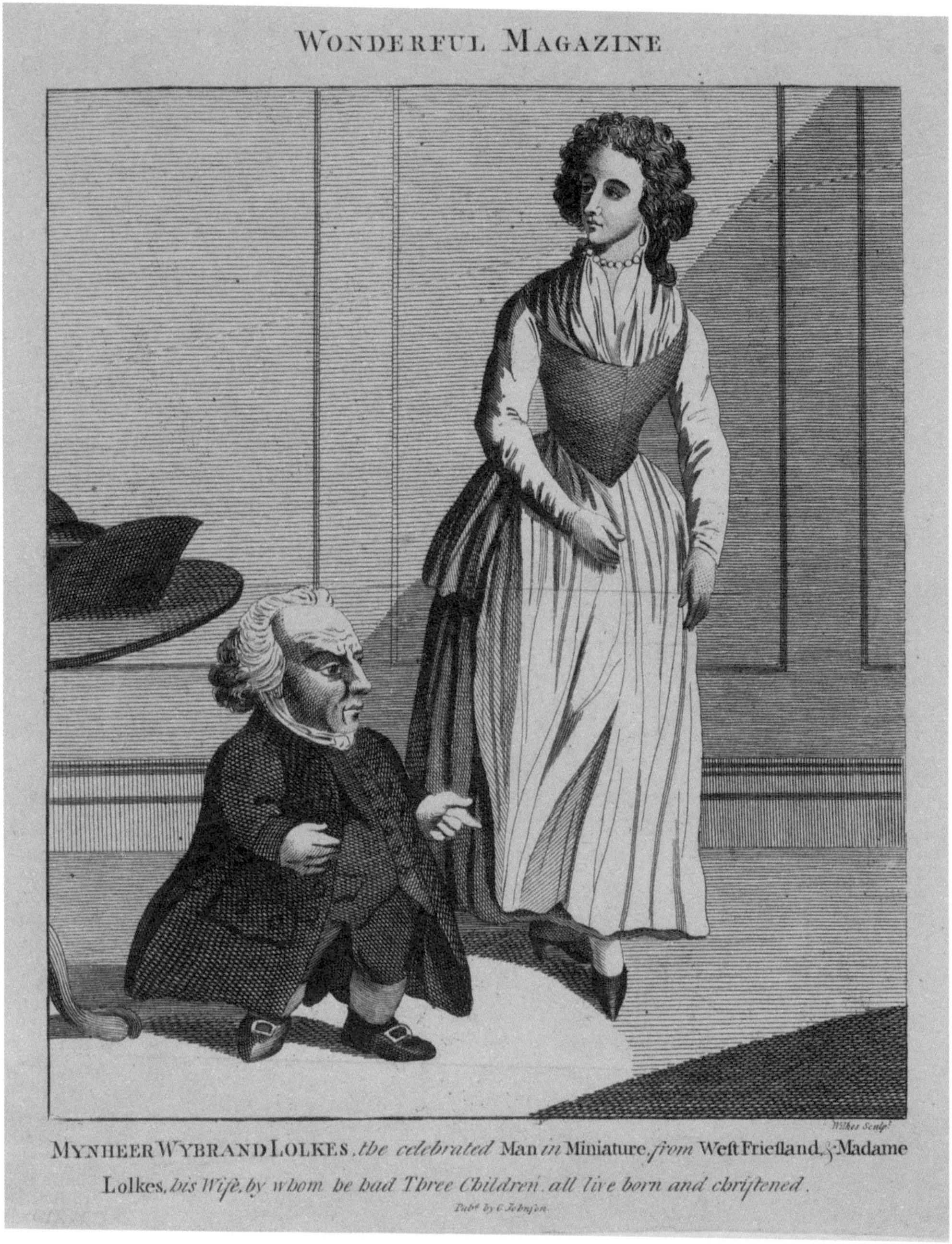
WONDERFUL MAGAZINE
Wilkes Sculp^t
MYNHEER WYBRAND LOLKES, the celebrated Man in Miniature, from West Friesland, & Madame Lolkes, his Wife, by whom he had Three Children, all live born and christened.
Pub^d by C. Johnson

Fig 16

ÆtatisSuæ.
17.

ISRAEL,
The Twin Brothers.

Fig 17

Lazarus Coloredo, a Genoese; aged 28.
(see Gent. Mag. p.482.)

Fig 18

Lazarus and Joannes Baptista Colloredo (b1617)

Fig 17 (left). Title on print: *Israel, the twin brothers*
Etching by unknown artist, 1634
Size: 19.8 cm x 14.7 cm

Fig 18 (left). Title on print: *Lazarus Coloredo*
Etching by unknown artist, 1645
Size: 17.5 cm x 11.5 cm
Published: for *Gentleman's Magazine*

Lazarus and Joannes Baptista Colloredo were born in 1617 in Genoa and exhibited professionally throughout Europe from their teenage years. Lazarus was described as a 'comely gentleman'[63] when he arrived in London in 1637 for an audience with Charles I to display the body of his 'parasitic twin', Joannes. After this sole appearance in London, they travelled widely around Britain, exhibiting in Norwich (1639) and Aberdeen (1642).

Joannes was said to breathe and salivate, but did not eat and his eyes were closed.[64] His name 'Joannes Baptista' suggests that he was baptised and so given the status of a separate individual. The brothers were the subject of great medical interest as doctors tried to detect signs of life in Joannes, and they were the subject of a report by the eminent professor of anatomy at Copenhagen, Thomas Bartholin (1616–80].[65]

The earlier image of the brothers (Fig 18) was created in 1634 when they were 17 years old, and the later image (Fig 19) in 1645, at the age of 28. These portraits would have been used as advertising outside exhibition venues.[66] The later image appeared in the *Gentlemen's Magazine* in 1777, revealing a long-standing public fascination with the brothers.

The cloak hanging from Lazarus' shoulders served as a curtain to 'hide' Joannes when not performing, allowing for a dramatic reveal during the exhibition. Lazarus often recounted a tale of murdering a man who had taunted him and subsequently evading execution by claiming that the innocent Joannes would also die.[67]

The *New Testament* parable of Jesus raising Lazarus from the dead taught a lesson of perseverance and the story of Lazarus is told only in the Gospel of St John ('Joannes'): these Biblical associations would have been immediately meaningful to 17th century audiences, giving viewers an opportunity to take home a moral lesson from their viewing. Despite the stress to his own body, Lazarus is said to have lived a normal life span and fathered several children.[68] ∎

Fig 19 (right). Mrs Everitt and Thomas Hills Everitt (b1779)
Title on print: *Mrs Everitt and her son, the gigantic infant*
Etching with stipple by unknown artist, 1780
Size: 28.8 cm x 21.1 cm
Published: W Richardson, London,
21 January 1780

Thomas Hills Everitt (or Everett) was born in February 1779, the son of the manager of a paper mill by the River Lea at Enfield, Middlesex. The image caption states that Thomas had been normal sized at birth but by 11 months, when this portrait was created, he was 3 feet 3 inches (107 cm) in height and measured 2 feet 6 inches (76 cm) around the chest. It also informs the viewer that Thomas 'lives entirely on the Breast, is healthy, and very good natur'd'.

Of the Everitt's five children, the eldest, a son aged 12, was small for his age, but the second, an unusually large boy, had died of measles at the age of 15 months.[69] Mr Sherwen, the local surgeon who measured baby Thomas, had been so impressed with him that he predicted that he was 'as likely to arrive at maturity (accidental diseases excepted)' as any child he ever saw.[70] Mrs Everitt lovingly holds her cherubic-looking baby and we wonder why she wished to exhibit him, but according to the *Gentleman's Magazine* it was Thomas's father's idea:

'The present subject (Thomas), being the second of the kind, excites a greater degree of curiosity, of which the father intends to avail himself, by carrying the child up to London, and making a public shew of him.'[71]

Thomas was exhibited daily from 11am until 4pm at Mr Owen's, a confectioner at 66 Cornhill. Unfortunately, 'the confined situation had such an effect on his health that he was soon brought back into his native air'.[72] This was a brief respite however, for Thomas was returned to London where he was exhibited continuously for over a month and died that same year (1780).[73] At this time, more than one in five babies died before reaching their first birthday. Perhaps Thomas would not have survived childhood, but it is likely that his sojourn in London and constant contact with the public contributed to cutting short his brief life. ■

Mrs EVERITT and her SON, ——— The GIGANTIC INFANT;

Born 7th Feby 1779, at Enfield Paper Mills, Middlesex;
whose true dimensions at the Age of Eleven Months, were as follows:

His height 3.3 — Round his Breast 2.6 — Loins 3.1 — Thigh 1.9 — Leg 1.2 — Arm 0.11 — Wrist 0.9

He is of a prodigious weight, lives entirely on the Breast, is healthy, and very good
natured, was not remarkably large when born, but since the Age of
five or six weeks, has increased to the amazing size he is now of.

London: Publish'd as the Act directs, 11 Jany 1780, by W. Richardson York House N°31 Strand

Fig 19

BLIND GRANNY.

Fig 20

62

Fig 20 (left). 'Blind Granny' (*c*17–18th century)
Title on print: *Blind Granny*
Stipple by unknown artist, date unknown
Size: 21.3 cm x 13.1 cm

The real name of this elderly lady is unknown, but she lived in London around the turn of the 18th century and was called 'Blind Granny' and even 'Lady Granny'. In this print she is shown wearing rough clothing. Her eyebrows are light (or white) – suggesting her 'granny' status – and her tongue protrudes from her parted lips.

Blind Granny was famous for her huge tongue (known medically today as macroglossia), with which she would lick her blind eye in return for money to buy beer.[74] It is not know whether her sight impairment was a result of licking her eye or some other reason.

Blind Granny was considered a 'character' in her locality and was celebrated in verses of the time:

'Yet, tho' her honor's now neglected,
She's merry still, no whit dejected;
Which shows that wit may be a trouble,
And only makes misfortune double,
While GRANNY always blith and jolly,
Enjoys the pleasure of her folly.'[75]

In this sense, 'folly' is used to describe mental health issues. She was accepted by the local population as an eccentric living within their midst, despite the proximity of Bethlem Hospital (known as 'Bedlam'), an institution for people commonly known as 'lunatics' from 1377 and which was traditionally a favourite resort for sightseers – 'the *frisson* of the freakshow'.[76]

Blind Granny holds a full tankard of ale and it is recorded that once she had drunk her fill in the local inn, she would dance frantically in the street to the amusement of the crowd until collapsing in doorways. People would sober her up by dousing her with pails of water and she would be followed by children who teased her.[77]

Where she lived or who looked after her is not known, but like many elderly people of this time she may have relied on alms or charity. ∎

Fig 21 (right). Joseph Clark (died *c*1650)
Title on print: *Joseph Clark*
Etching by unknown artist, *c*1792
Size: 14.5 cm x 10 cm

Joseph Clark lived in Pall Mall, London, during the first half of the 17th century.

He was a contortionist and described as 'the most extraordinary Posture Master that ever existed who exhibited every species of deformity and dislocation'. His nickname was 'the wandering tumour'.[78] Apparently, Clark had been able to contort his limbs and face since childhood, which suggests that he had what doctors might now label 'hypermobility' or subluxation of the joints. In other words what would have once been considered a 'talent' or 'wonder' has been medicalised.

Clark entertained by performing feats of contortion. With his 'absolute command of all his muscles and joints' and ability to 'disjoint almost his whole body' he could be hunch backed, pot bellied or sharp breasted.[79] He would trick people such as tailors who had measured his 'normal' body for clothes, by claiming that they had measured him incorrectly.[80] He would also beg as a disabled person from people he knew, and he was so convincing that they did not recognise him.[81] It was said that the 'powers of his face were more extraordinary than the flexibility of his body'.[82] In this way, Clark was able to assume a number of identities. Apparently, James Moleyns (*c*1580–1638), a famous surgeon of the day, was so shocked at the sight of Clark that he would not attempt a cure – not that he could cure him anyway.[83]

Clark was mentioned by the diarist and writer, John Evelyn (1620–1706) in his book, *Numismate* (1697), and his fame lasted well into the 18th century, as attested by this image dated 1792.

Clark's 'spinal curvature' gives the appearance of a hunchback with protruding abdomen. His right foot is twisted backwards and he is poking out his tongue. He wears a buttoned jerkin, knee breeches, stockings and buckled shoes. A key is tied to his jerkin by a cord looped through a button hole. Images of this sort, which appeared in *Wonderful Magazine*, might be put up in public places such as coffee shops or taverns. ∎

JOSEPH CLARK.

Fig 21

THE LIVING HETERADELPH,
OR
DUPLEX BOY.

Fig 22

66

Fig 22 (left). 'Heteradelph' or 'Duplex Boy' (b1857)
Title on print: *The living heteradelph, or duplex boy*
Lithograph by unknown artist, date unknown
Size: 19.3 cm x 13 cm
Published: J Gilbert, London, *c*1865

This boy was known as a 'Heteradelph', 'Duplex' or 'double-bodied' child. His name is unknown, but he was born in 1857, the ninth child of a Lancashire family.[84]

His parents (who wished to remain anonymous) 'gave' him to Dr Joseph Kahn's Anatomical and Pathological Museum at 4 Coventry Street, Leicester Square, London. Having a disabled child was historically often considered a punishment for a parent's sins; families could be avoided by their communities and the child's inability to work would have been a financial burden.

Dr Kahn had opened his museum in 1851 and it became the most visited public museum of anatomy. Public interest in anatomy had been heightened following the scandal of the Edinburgh murders committed by Burke and Hare to obtain bodies for anatomists in 1827–8. The boy was exhibited three times daily at noon, two and four o'clock and viewing him was relatively expensive, at two shillings and sixpence[85] – the audiences would have included medical practitioners. Dr Kahn accompanied the exhibition of the child with a lecture where he criticised the widely accepted theory of 'maternal imagination', that malformations of the fetus were caused by the mother's imagination.

A pamphlet written by Dr Kahn, which would have been for sale at the time of viewing, stated that:

'A few years ago we would have spoken of it as a freak of nature, and called it, in scientific language, a lusus naturae but modern science has shewn us, that phenomena are presented to our notice in the varied and ever-changing paranormal of organic life, and are as much as result of a fixed and immutable law, as the revolving of a planet, the appearance of an eclipse or the reverberations of a thunder peal.'

Dr Kahn's Museum was closed in 1873 after it was successfully prosecuted under the Obscene Publications Act of 1857, and many of the 500 exhibits including models showing the destructive effect of syphilis were destroyed.

There is no further information available on the boy or how long he lived. ∎

Fig 23 (right). John Valerius (b1667)
Title on print: *John Valerius (born without arms)*
Etching by R Grave, 1698
Size: 15.2 cm x 9.6 cm
Published: Holland, 1698

John Valerius was born in Germany in 1667. He was born with no arms but with a vestigial thumb extruding from his right shoulder. Valerius lived with his parents until their death when he started exhibiting himself to earn a living. He came to England in 1698 and left between 1705 and 1710. It is not known how widely he travelled around Britain, but he did show himself in London.[86]

This image is a self-portrait at the age of 31. It is a copy of the frontispiece of Valerius' limited edition book (published in Holland) which includes 16 images (all self-portraits) depicting him performing a number of activities, including firing a musket, holding a sword, beating a drum, writing, picking his hat up off the ground and playing cards and dice, with descriptions in Dutch.[87] Most of the drawings showed typical masculine activities of the time, highlighting Valerius's independence and manliness.

If it was not for his name caption, we might be confused over the portrayal of gender. As Valerius chose to represent himself in this manner, can we therefore assume that it is a true likeness? A version of this image was published in London in 1819 by RS Kirby, suggesting that Valerius remained a subject of some interest throughout the 18th and beginning of the 19th centuries.

Valerius was well-educated and could write in five languages. He was also highly dexterous, writing with both of his feet and his mouth.[88] As an additional element to his bodily exhibition, Valerius would provide his paying audience with specimens of his writing, created while they watched. Sir William Musgrave (1655–1721), a fellow of the Royal College of Physicians, reputedly owned a portrait of Valerius who had written four lines on the back of it, using his feet. ∎

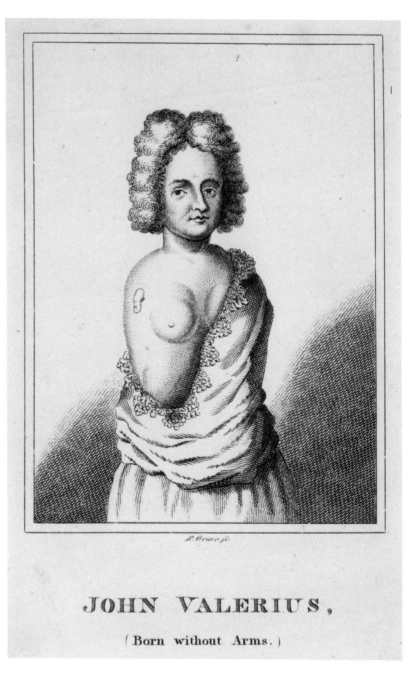

JOHN VALERIUS,

(Born without Arms.)

Fig 23

Fig 24 (right). Henry Blacker (b1724)
Title on print: *Mr Henry Blacker the British giant*
Engraving with etching by unknown artist, date
unknown
Size: 19.6 cm x 11.4 cm
Published: C Johnson

Henry Blacker was born near Cuckfield in Sussex in
1724.[89] The image caption claims that at 'seven
feet four inches tall' he was 'the tallest man ever
exhibited in England'. Recorded heights, however,
vary between sources and were often embellished
by the exhibiting individuals. Amongst the many
foreign exhibitors, the English Blacker was a
favourite with the public and styled himself the
'British giant'.

There is little information about his early life, but
Blacker started his exhibiting career himself in
London in 1751. Much was made of Blacker's
appearance – he did not have the physical
features common to 'giants' such as the knock
knees, large hands and big feet,[90] and was
considered more attractive.

This image shows Blacker with people of average
size – making him appear even taller. Blacker had
a large base of fans in London including William,
Duke of Cumberland (1721–65), also a tall man.

Blacker left London in 1752, but returned the
same year when an exhibition announced in the
Daily Advertiser, 8 December 1752, described him
as the 'Modern Colossus' or 'Wonderful Giant'.
It noted that he could be seen at a room in Half
Moon Court joining Ludgate. Blacker worked long
hours, exhibiting himself between 9am and 9pm
most days. The advertisement noted:

'This phenomenon in nature hath already had
the honour of being inspected by great numbers
of the nobility and gentry, by men of the Royal
Society, and several gentlemen and ladies who
are lovers of natural curiosities; who allow him to
be of stupendous height and affirm him to be the
best proportioned of his size they ever saw.'

The advertisement ended with a note that Mr
Blacker had lost a boot and would pay three
shillings for its return.[91] We know very little about
Blacker after his exhibiting career ended. ∎

Mr Henry Blacker the BRITISH GIANT.

Born near Cuckfield in Sussex 1724. He is thought by all who have view'd him, to be the tallest Man ever exhibited in England, measuring 7 Feet 4 Inches & exceeds ȳ famous Mynheer Cajanus who was shewn with so much Applause several Years ago

Publ.d by C. Johnson.

Fig 24

JAMES PORO,

(Born at Genoa 1686.)

Maddocks sculp.

Fig 25

72

Fig 25 (left). James and Matthew Poro (b1686)
Title on print: *James Poro*
Stipple by Maddocks, date unknown
Size: 18.3 cm x 12.7 cm

———————————————————————

James Poro was born in Genoa in 1686 and exhibited in London in 1714.[92] He attracted the attention of Sir Hans Sloane (1660–1755), physician, botanist and founder of the British Museum, who had Poro's portrait painted.[93]

In this image, a fashionably dressed and bewigged Poro stares abstractedly into the distance while exposing his 'parasitic' twin who was baptised Matthew.[94] The twin is fixed to Poro's abdomen, but bears little resemblance to a human except for a rudimentary face and protruding teeth. Matthew's hair has been plaited and dressed with bows. These may be false plaits, but the fact that both the teeth and the hair have grown (both are composed of the substance keratin) suggests that it is the twin's real hair. The parasitic twin was said to 'possess an independent animated nature to himself' and had therefore been baptised[95]– given the status of a separate individual. The word 'parasitic' is a modern term and would not have been used in the 17th or 18th century.

In Poro's day, the terms 'monster' and 'sport of nature'[96] were used to denote the belief that there was some divine intervention at work. Perhaps his parents were blamed for committing a sin that was then re-visited on their son in such a physical manifestation as to be a permanent reminder of it. What is going through James's mind as he poses for this portrait? Is this the pose he assumes when confronted with a gawping audience?

It is interesting that both James and Matthew Poro and the Colloredo brothers (b1617) (Figs 17 and 18, p58) were said to have been born in Genoa. Was it a coincidence that this small Italian republic witnessed the birth of such rarities within a 70-year period or has legend mingled with fact? The incidence of conjoined twins is one in 50,000–100,000 births. Parasitic twins may be twice as rare. ■

Fig 26 (right). Johann Kleyser
c17th–18th century
Title on print: *J Kleyser* ⁻
Aquatint by unknown artist, *c*1718
Size: 10 cm x 5.4 cm

This man is named as Johann Kleyser on the Showhistory website[97] and he probably came from Germany. The portrait, which depicts a solemn-faced man past youth wearing a fine wig and feathered hat, states that Kleyser exhibited himself in London in 1718. The rest of his attire is very informal. He wears a sleeveless shirt and is bare-footed with stockings that have probably been cut off at the ankle to allow use of his feet and toes in place of hands and fingers. Kleyser is said to have been born without arms.

He was a highly intelligent and gifted man, but like many who exhibited themselves it was not enough for an audience just to witness his body: he had to put on a performance. Visitors who came to see him were entertained by Kleyser writing 'very finely with his mouth and right and left foot, in five different languages'. He also shaved and combed his hair with his right foot, walked on his two big toes and balanced on one toe. He would hop on one leg whilst the other was draped around his neck.[98] The small size of this image suggests that it was produced as a promotional handbill or souvenir. In terms of Kleyser's stated intellectual gifts, such as the ability to write in five languages, he has much in common with John Valerius (b1667) (Fig 23, p69), an earlier showman also born with no arms. Since they were almost contemporaries and may indeed have been alive at the same time, it is likely that the legendary feats of one merged with the other in showbusiness promotion.

Nothing is known of Kleyser's personal life or who travelled with him, but he was probably on the professional touring circuit of the time, perhaps eventually returning to his native country after making as much money as possible. ∎

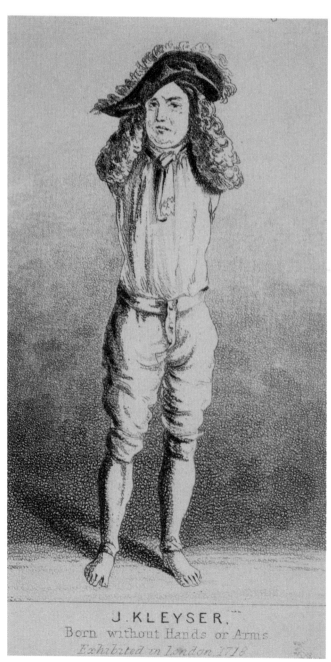

J. KLEYSER.
Born without Hands or Arms.
Exhibited in London 1718.

Fig 26

Fig 27

Fig 27 (left). Richard Gibson (1615–90) (?)
Title on painting frame: *A dwarf*
Oil painting by unknown artist (after Sir Peter Lely), 19th century
Size: 90 cm x 74 cm

This painting is believed to be of Richard Gibson, although it has not been categorically identified as him.

Richard Gibson's birthplace is uncertain, but he was first employed as a page to 'a Lady at Mortlack' (or Mortlake) who noticed his talent for drawing and apprenticed him to Francis Cleyn (c1582–1658) at Mortlake tapestry works. Gibson was already a limner (miniaturist) when he joined the service of Philip Herbert, fourth Earl of Pembroke. His future wife, Ann Sheppard (married 14 February 1641), was also in this household. Both Gibson and his wife were of short stature. Gibson's height was 3 feet 10 inches (117 cm).[99]

Gibson moved in exalted circles and became wealthy and eminent, signing his paintings 'RG' and 'DG' (Dwarf Gibson). He was associated with the courts of Charles I, Charles II and James II, who appointed him drawing master to his daughters, Mary and Anne.[100] When Mary married William of Orange (1677), the Gibsons accompanied her to The Hague, returning to London when she and her husband succeeded to the British throne (1688).

In this oil portrait of Gibson, painted in the 19th century by an anonymous artist, he is depicted asleep in a red and gold painted chair. He is wearing a brown suit and cloak. His buttoned jacket has black (perhaps velvet) turned-back cuffs. A white shirt with collar and long, full sleeves peeks out from the jacket. A portrait of Gibson by Sir Peter Lely (1618–80), in the National Portrait Gallery, also shows him wearing a brown suit and white shirt although in that painting the suit appears to be of satin. In general, the 19th century painting is somewhat crudely executed and shows Gibson to have a very pronounced snub nose and large ungainly head, features that are not reproduced in any other likeness of him.

Richard and Anne Gibson had five children, of whom at least three became limners. When Gibson died on 20 July 1690, they seem to have been living with their daughter, Susannah-Penelope, in Henrietta Street, Covent Garden, London.[101] ■

Fig 28 (right). 'The Twin Brothers' (born *c*1693)
Title on print: *The twin brothers*
Aquatint by unknown artist, *c*1716
Size: 10 cm x 5.3 cm

Conjoined twins were often the source of fascination for both the medical profession and the general public. 'The Twin Brothers' exhibited in London in 1716 when they were about 23 years old.[102] Not much is known about them; even their names remain a mystery, and there is no information about where they were from. It is likely that they travelled around England, making their living from exhibiting themselves.

There was little differentiation by the medical profession between conjoined twins and parasitic twins. Both would have been considered *monstrum* (from the Latin *monere*, to warn), meaning a miracle, a wonder or divine portent.[103,104] It was believed by some authorities that such births served as an omen for a future event or that they imparted a heavenly message. Conjoined twins, for example, were often considered to be God's reminder of the close 'brotherly love' that people should show to one another.

'The Twin Brothers' were different to a number of twins seen in England in the 17th century – unlike the Colloredo brothers (b1617) (Figs 17 and 18, p58) 'The Twin Brothers' were both able to speak. According to the reports we have of 'The Twin Brothers', the biggest of the two was

'... born a perfect man, well-proportioned and from his right side issued a little above his hip, a body of a man from the middle upward, perfectly shaped with hands, arms and head. He could eat and drink with good appetite, could speak distinctly and had very good sight.'[105]

The small image shown here is probably a copy of a postcard, which would have been sold as a souvenir for the paying public to remember their visit to see the twins. ∎

Fig 28

Contemporary photographic portraits of disabled participants

A collaboration between the photographer Lynn Weddle and the focus group participants

'Disability has influenced my art by default! I don't define myself by my disability, that's for others.'

Debbie Allaire from Chepstow, Wales
Acquiring a visible disability 12 years ago was a shock! If I had had my disability at birth, it's unlikely I'd be a designer. None of the art colleges I trained in or subsequently taught at were accessible. More to the point, I learned to design furniture without consideration of who might sit in it. Disability has influenced my art by default! I don't define myself by my disability, that's for others. My lack of functioning legs is not an impediment to enjoying myself, much to others' surprise. The Royal College of Physicians' project is interesting as many in our society define disability as a negative state; this project has revealed it has not always been so. Fascinatingly, some people born with a disability in the past were able to make a good living. Not now: disabled people who gain a lot of money are those that have acquired a disability that an insurer deem worthy of compensation. ■

Jamie Beddard from London

I am currently working as a freelance artist, having recently left my post as a diversity officer at the Arts Council. I both direct and perform, and am an experienced workshop leader and trainer. My employers include London Metropolitan University, the National Youth Theatre and a variety of drama colleges. Previously, I was an associate director of Graeae Theatre Company, and editor of *Disability Arts in London (DAIL)* magazine. My TV/film acting credits include *Skalligrigg, Quills, All the King's Men, Wonderful You, Common As Muck* and *The Egg*. My theatre credits include *Carrie's War, Waiting For Godot, Ubu, Volpone, The Fly* and *The Freakshow*. Much of my work concerns the plethora of identities we inhabit, labels we are given and how we are represented. The historical similarities, differences and echoes unearthed through this project have been of particular interest. ∎

'... my work concerns the ... identities we inhabit, labels we are given and how we are represented.'

'Losing my hearing in mid-life was a monumental transition, threatening my whole identity. I felt excluded

Margot Bristow from Brighton

I was interested in the similarities and differences when viewing disability from 1600 to 2010. I particularly focused on the hidden disability of deafness, especially in the light of having read a book by Lennard J Davis,[106] in which he writes about how 'normalcy' is enforced on people with disabilities and the deaf. I myself regularly experience being marginalised, as if I were in some way oblivious to the world around me. Losing my hearing in mid-life was a monumental transition, threatening my whole identity. I felt excluded and isolated. The experience of trying to fathom the spoken word and other people's distorted expressions and impatience has led to my feelings of alienation at times. Finally, I have become a lip-reader and have a wonderful hearing dog who accompanies me everywhere. He has given me back my confidence and introduces people to my disability. Having worked as an art therapist and teacher, I am now a freelance artist and photographer. ∎

Hayley Davies from Poole

I am currently volunteering at the National Archives. I have knowledge and experience of working within disability arts, and have a keen interest in art and history. I was particularly interested in taking part in the Royal College of Physicians' project to look at the prints from an artistic and historical view. Having a disability myself, it was a great opportunity to be able to discuss the historical changes in perceptions of people with disabilities, and see how disabled people were represented, or how they chose to represent themselves, over the years. Being involved in this project also gave me a chance to express my own views, choose how I wanted to be represented, and to continue to develop my own artistic practice. ■

' ... this project also gave me a chance to express my own views, choose how I wanted to be represented ... '

Focus group session

Tim Gebbels from London
I was educated at special schools for visually impaired kids at both primary and secondary level before reading modern history at Queen's College, Oxford. The choice of potential career paths is not extensive if you're blind, and on leaving university I trod water for a year, doing soft bits of journalism, before getting a job in BBC Radio Drama. This was a subject I did genuinely know quite a lot about, as it had been a passion since I was small. I've been a professional actor for over 10 years and, although work's thin just now, I can't really imagine doing anything else. My hobbies include reading novels, cricket, *Doctor Who*, and target shooting (with an air rifle over 10 metres). I love my dog and my friends. Jane Austen said there are only two forces in the world, love and money, and she was so right. ■

'I've been a professional actor for over 10 years
... I can't really imagine doing anything else.'

Miro Griffiths from Wirral

I am a 21-year-old postgraduate student, completing a masters in disability studies at the University of Leeds. I also manage my own company, Miro Consultancy. As a disability consultant, I travel across the United Kingdom, and occasionally internationally. I speak and advise on a range of issues relating to disability, especially around the importance of participation and empowerment issues, and the transitional stages of a disabled person's life. I chose to be involved in the Royal College of Physicians' project as I feel that art, along with the media, has a vital role when discussing the issue of disability equality. I have a neuromuscular condition (spinal muscular atrophy type two), which means I use a power-wheelchair. In my spare time I like to socialise with friends in Liverpool and spend time with my partner, Marija, a medical student in Zagreb, Croatia. ■

'... I feel that art, along with the media, has a vital role when discussing the issue of disability equality.'

'A key theme that recurs within my writing is how disability has been written out of the history of art.'

Colin Hambrook from Hove

I am currently acting manager/editor of *Disability Arts Online*, which is dedicated to showcasing the artistic practice of disabled artists and performers, and publishes ideas, reviews, discussion and blogs which reflect on our lives as disabled people. Over the past 17 years, I have worked as a disability arts consultant and arts writer on a variety of web and print-based publications, including *Dada-News*, *Architecture Inside Out*, *NorDaf News*, Channel 4 programme support and *Disability Arts In London (DAIL)* magazine. A key theme that recurs within my writing is how disability has been written out of the history of art. I am fascinated by the idea of uncovering untold histories of the lives of disabled people, and looking at how much has changed and how much remains the same in terms of disability representation. This Royal College of Physicians project is an important step in uncovering little seen and little known archives, and creating a contemporary context for those images. ■

'I have a problem with pigeon-holing people and would like to do away with "-isms" and "-bilities"...

Margaret Hughes from Wigan
As a member of the RCP's Patient and Carer Network and my work within the voluntary sector, I am constantly looking at ways to increase disability awareness and access. I have a congenital joint problem, multiple epiphyseal dysplasia, which has at different times in my life confined me to a wheelchair, had me mobile only with walking aids of various kinds, and occasionally made me house-bound. Now, thanks to medical science and the NHS, I have four artificial joints and am fully mobile, although constantly in pain. I also have ulcerative colitis, which is in remission at present, so outwardly I look fine. So, although I consider myself to be less able than some people, my problems are hidden, which causes some difficulties with inconsiderate people. I have a problem with pigeon-holing people and would like to do away with '-isms' and '-bilities', and opt instead for respect, tolerance and consideration for all. I can dream. ■

Christiana Joseph from London
I am a black woman born in London of Afrikan descent. I decided to apply to the project as my previous experience has shown women, and in particular black women, are under-represented in the arts and media industry. As a woman with a disability, I find some respite and enjoyment in the various art forms available to me. I visit galleries and exhibitions, and attend the theatre. My past work with young people has been creative in nature, including drama therapy, and sand and water therapy. These helped gain the trust of the young people and helped move their lives on in a positive way. I intend to continue with developing my creative pathway. I have studied journalism and script writing, and have worked as a school governor and supported many community projects. ■

' ... women, and in particular black women, are under-represented in the arts and media industry.'

' ... when I acquired a physical disability ... [I] had my eyes opened to life as a disabled person.

Adam Lotun from Surrey

I have been working in the disability field and campaigning for disability rights since 1991, when I acquired a physical disability and had my eyes opened to life as a disabled person. I was also born with a learning disability and medical condition, which were not diagnosed until very late in my life. I therefore received no special treatment or resources whilst I was growing up and did not realise that I had developed coping strategies to manage my disability at home, in school and in the workplace. I studied law with particular reference to the Disability Discrimination Act. My early career was within the Civil Service, working to develop the Access to Work Service across the United Kingdom. I have since worked as a disability employment adviser in job centres in London, and have worked at a senior level with government ministers, advising on strategies, including employment issues.

Julie McNamara
from Birkenhead, Merseyside

When this project was brought to my attention, I leapt at the chance to get involved. I'm a playwright and theatre producer. I work with excluded voices in the margins of our communities; voices with extraordinary stories to tell. Museums, libraries and institutions store incredible collections that reveal glimpses of extraordinary lives. I've recently been working on a production called *Crossings*, exploring the impact of forced migration and sexual slavery. So I was immediately drawn to the image of John Boby in this collection. I wondered if he had skilfully evaded the greedy hands of the plantation owners? Or was he a freed slave who earned his fortune allowing folks to marvel at his skin? And it is clear he became an object of wonder rather than ridicule – hence the title of his portrait – *The wonderful spotted Indian*! ■

'Museums, libraries and institutions store incredible collections that reveal glimpses of extraordinary lives.'

'I am compelled to challenge the negative, disabling and stigmatising stereotypes of disability ... '

Aidan Moesby from Tyne and Wear
Artist, poet, gardener and dreamer: my work explores identity and memory (personally and in the cultural, collective sense), how we deal with our psychologic heritage, and the relationship between ourselves and the world around us. I have a studio in the Shed, Gateshead, where I indulge my passion for letterpress and all things text. There is a tree in a small corner of New Zealand that will forever be 'home'. I wish people would turn off their mobiles/laptops and enjoy the journey more. I am wholly nourished by my partner, garden and hens. Staring out the window constitutes a valuable part of the creative process and is not time wasted. Disability has been the catalyst to re-evaluate my life. I am compelled to challenge the negative, disabling and stigmatising stereotypes of disability, particularly around mental health. To that end, I create art, mentor, train and lecture. ∎

Mark Pampel from London

I have Usher syndrome type three A, which is an inherited, rare disorder of the eyes and ears, resulting in severe sight impairment and hearing problems. However, I can still manage to do some work as a music specialist. I started playing the piano at five, and now occasionally perform at two restaurants and at local day centres, providing background piano music at mealtimes. I run a music workshop at a centre for people with mental health issues, and also play the harpsichord at Fenton House Museum, Hampstead, during the summer. Some of my compositions are available to listen to on MySpace. I serve on various charity committees, at a local and national level. I practise transcendental meditation and yoga regularly, to help maintain my general health and well-being. ■

'I run a music workshop at a centre for people with mental health issues, and also play the harpsichord ...'

LIFT
Not
By Bread
Alone

Matthew Buchinger, 1724

Focus group session

Saleem A Quadri from London

I was born in Hyderabad, India. Throughout my life, I have been inspired by my dear parents. My mother was a painter and my father was a doctor/surgeon. I came to England in 1966 and studied art in Birmingham. Further study at the Royal College of Arts, London, cemented my true vocation as an artist. Since 1982, I have had both solo and group exhibitions of my work in the UK and abroad. My work is included in several public collections, notably Tate Britain, Manchester City Art Gallery and Birmingham Museum and Art Gallery (see www.saleem-arif-quadri.co.uk). In 2008, I was awarded an MBE for my services to the arts. My recent disability brought new challenges to my career, but family support and my innate determination enabled me to discover new avenues of creativity. My curating and creative work continues with renewed energy and a positive outlook. Meeting other creative disabled people, sharing ideas, but most importantly learning from them, was indeed a unique aspect of the Royal College of Physicians' project. ■

Penny Pepper from London

I am a writer, spoken word performer/ storyteller, singer and film-maker. I have a long history within the disability arts movement under various guises, engaged in numerous creative acts and provocations. I have been a published writer for over 15 years. I use performance skills, gained from training with Graeae Theatre Company, and work with cellist Jo Cox, melding poetic rhythms with musical colour, which makes my spoken word work unique. I am a regular performer on the spoken word circuit. Recently, I modelled for visual artist Tanya Raabe on a project exploring the disabled female nude and identity. I also sit for art photographer Larry Dunstan, whose work examines the bodies of those defined by the mainstream as 'different'. I enjoy modelling as an act of defiance against accepted female physical norms and because it links to many of the themes I explore within my writing. ∎

'... I modelled for visual artist Tanya Raabe on a projec exploring the disabled female nude and identity.'

' ... to give opportunities to disabled and deaf artists, to enable them to become more visible in society.'

Patricia Place from London

My professional mission has been to increase and sustain access in its widest sense for all disabled and deaf people. I have always been a catalyst for action. I have worked primarily in the voluntary sector, and use the arts to give opportunities to disabled and deaf artists, to enable them to become more visible in society. I believe the work has had a real impact on the lives of the artists, as children, young people and adults, and has helped challenge attitudes and alter people's perceptions of how disabled people are viewed by the non-disabled majority. ■

'I feel passionate about the empowering possibilities of passing on ... life stories, skills, knowledge and experience'

Liz Porter from Hove

I am a visually impaired performance storyteller, arts developer and disability adviser. One of my current ventures is working with English Heritage on Creative Landscapes (an Accentuate project that explores creative ways to make heritage more accessible to all). I feel passionate about the empowering possibilities of passing on our life stories, skills, knowledge and experience. I love to explore the representation of disability through stories. Our stories, our images of ourselves, enrich our lives and form a central part of the cultural fabric of the social history of disability. They matter and are a strong source of inspiration to me. It's been fascinating to hear the stories behind the historic portraits on display in this Royal College of Physicians project. This project has also given me the opportunity to have pictures taken of myself that explore my disability and how I represent myself in a new and more imaginative way. ■

Julia Poser from London

I have a degree in genetics. I have been fascinated by science since I was a child. My other great passion is classical music, especially Schubert and Mozart. Apart from loving the music, it makes me more aware of physical sensations and calms some of the unpleasant sensations and stiffness associated with my cerebral palsy. I am happy and proud to be an aunt. Freddie, aged 10, and Rosie, aged eight, help me when I am with them, but watching them grow up and move is even better. Some of my movements and understanding of life have got better as I have got older. I was very interested in seeing how people coped with their conditions in the past and what brought them to the attention of the Royal College of Physicians. I do hope this project helps disabled people in the future. ∎

'Some of my movements and understanding of life have got better as I have got older.'

'I have performed ... in several productions with Graeae and other companies, and am also a writer.'

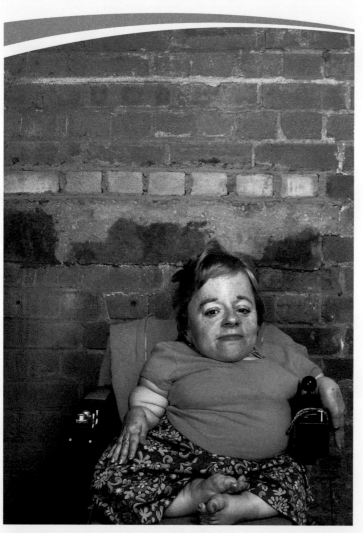

Sophie Partridge from London

I boarded at school in Hampshire from 11 to 18, and then joined Creative Young (disabled) People Together, a charity patroned by Nabil Shaban, which was, in fact, a small bungalow in Bracklesham Bay, West Sussex ... the end of the earth! The strange thing was that, despite the smallness of the place, it was there that my horizons began to broaden and I began to wonder what to do with my life. I went on to college and got a degree in English literature with art. In the autumn of 1999 a fortuitous star shone when Graeae Theatre Company ran its first training course for disabled actors: I auditioned and was offered a place on the course. I have performed professionally in several productions with Graeae and other companies, and am also a writer. My first commission for Graeae, *Just Me, Bell*, an interactive piece for young people, toured schools in autumn 2009. ■

Mik Scarlet from London

I was born in 1965. I began my career as a musician, and performed in various bands as a singer and keyboard player throughout Europe. I moved into broadcasting in 1986, and was one of the first disabled people to present on mainstream TV. I worked for over 10 years in the BBC's Disability Programmes Unit, as a presenter and journalist, and presented the Emmy award-winning and BAFTA-nominated C4 kids show *Beat that*. I also wrote the theme tune for the *From the edge* series, and have acted in shows such as *The bill* and *2.4 children*. I am currently working as a journalist, musician and DJ, and am about to publish my autobiography. I am happily married and live in Camden with my wife, Diane. ■

'I am currently working as a journalist, musician and DJ, and am about to publish my autobiography.'

' ... I have always been interested in how we think about images of the body and the disabled person.

Michael Shamash from London
I decided to take part in the Royal College of Physicians' project because I have always been interested in how we think about images of the body and the disabled person. The 'differently able' person is a constant, continuously illuminating our awareness of how the concept of disability is constructed. As a person of restricted growth, I am aware of how so much of society's perceptions of those who are viewed as different are formed by prejudice and stereotype. I challenge those myths in my current job increasing service user participation in the East End of London. I have written about disability and its representation for a wide variety of journals specialising in the subject of disability, fashion and image. I lecture on the role that the disabled person plays in society at Middlesex University. This discussion shows both how much has changed and yet how much remains the same. ■

Jane Stemp from Somerset

I am the author of two novels, and have spoken and written on the representation of disabled people in children's fiction. Both my fiction and my research in this area are informed by my experience of living with cerebral palsy and hearing impairment. I am a graduate of Somerville College, Oxford, where I studied old and middle English. I have a long-standing interest in social and medical history and, under my married name, Jane Wickenden, curate the historic collections library at the Institute of Naval Medicine, Gosport. I have also worked on the historical books at the Royal College of Physicians. In my spare time I cook, travel and occasionally sail with the Jubilee Sailing Trust. ■

'Both my fiction and my research ... are informed by my experience of living with cerebral palsy ... '

Allan Sutherland from London

I was once described as 'the first political stand-up on the disability arts circuit' and for 30 years I have been exploring ways of making the voices of disabled people heard, including stand-up comedy, performance poetry, radio and television scriptwriting and journalism. My book, *Disabled we stand*,[107] helped many people to identify as disabled. My current work explores transcription poetry, creating sets of poems from oral history interviews with disabled people. I have recently been writer in residence at the Centre for Citizen Participation, Brunel University; this work can be read on the website *Disability Arts Online*. As a former film critic for *Sight and Sound, Time Out* and *Disability Now*, I have a long-standing interest in the representation of disabled people and, with film-maker Steven Dwoskin, organised the UK's first season of films about disability, *Carry on cripple* at the National Film Theatre in 1981. ■

' ... for 30 years I have been exploring ways of making the voices of disabled people heard ...

Project film makers
Bim Ajadi and Ted Evans

Karen Sutherland from Edinburgh

I have always aimed at seeing things differently. This started around the age of 12, when I took part in a documentary which gave me an amazing amount of confidence to speak up about some of the issues I feel passionate about as a young disabled person. Through working with film and photography, I have been able to express myself, show people how I feel, and show myself the way I want to been seen. I am currently working on a project with young disabled people in Scotland, looking at identity and self image, body and sexuality. Using creative techniques, such as film and photos, can empower them to see themselves in a positive way. When I found out about the Royal College of Physicians' project, I thought it would be fantastic experience and a good way of sharing views and experiences. ■

'Through working with film and photography, I have been able to express myself, show people how I feel ...

'I also compose music inspired by my sensory hypersensitivity and perception of my environment.'

Anya Ustaszewski from Hove

I am on the autistic spectrum. I currently work as a music mentor and workshop facilitator for disabled children, and as an autism and disability equality trainer. I previously worked as an access officer at the Royal Academy of Arts. I also compose music inspired by my sensory hypersensitivity and perception of my environment. I have given recitals at the House of Commons and have also performed my own music at various events, including the 2009 Decibel Performing Artists Showcase. I am an executive committee member of ASSERT Brighton and Hove, an organisation which provides support to people with Asperger syndrome and high functioning autism, and their relatives, partners and carers. I am also a steering committee member of the London Autistic Rights Movement and a member of the online community Spectrumites. I was the vice chair of the External Reference Group for the Autism Strategy. ■

'I worked for the NHS for 20 years, with the exception of three years with the Home Office.

Phil Willan
from the Ribble Valley, Lancashire
I am 56 and live in a cottage in a hilltop village in the Ribble Valley, Lancashire. I received a second renal transplant in 1983. I have had many other interventions, including gastric surgery, cardiac surgery, two hip replacements, removal of two cataracts, skin cancer excisions and other surgical procedures. I worked for the NHS for 20 years, with the exception of three years with the Home Office. My last post was that of north west regional manager for the National Treatment Agency for Substance Misuse. Since retiring in 2005, I have become a lay member of a number of committees and working groups under the auspices of the Royal College of Physicians. I am also a member of three expert advisory groups for the Medicines and Healthcare products Regulatory Agency. My interests include current affairs, classic cars, photography, the arts, good food, good beer and good wine. ∎

Anna C Young from London

I am passionate about the personalised delivery of care and the independence that comes from having direct payments. I have cerebral palsy and as a result have had to use a wheelchair. I also have mental health issues. None of this prevents me from living as full a life as I possibly can. This includes freelance journalism, and I have written pieces for a number of social care publications. I have been involved in the training of social workers for the Tavistock Clinic and University College London. I always make a point of emphasising the need for partnership working between those who need to use social care services and those who design and deliver them. However, recent experiences have taught me, in quite a harsh way, the gap that exists between the rhetoric of personalisation and the day-to-day reality for someone who needs support to live independently. ■

'I have been involved in the training of social workers for the Tavistock Clinic and University College London.'

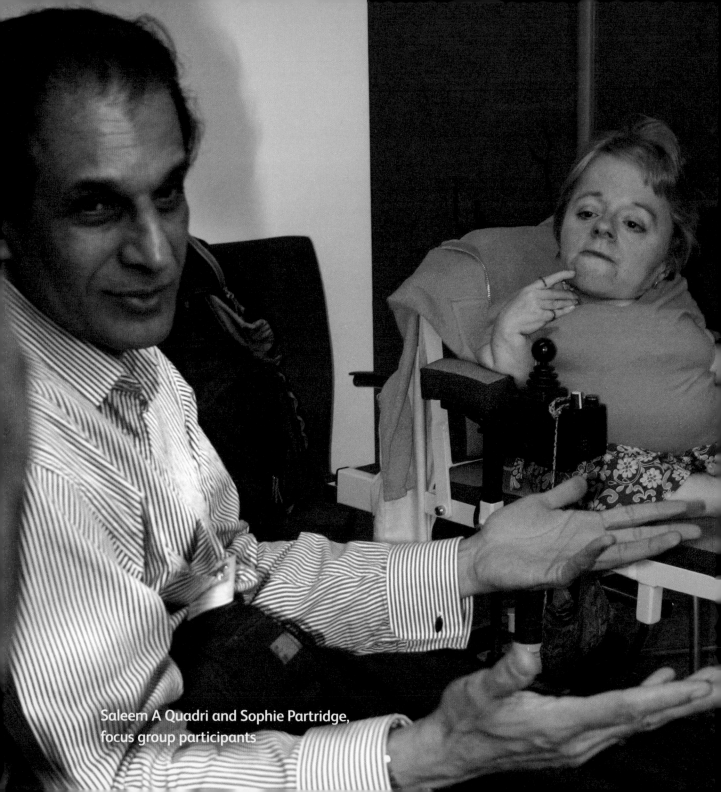

Saleem A Quadri and Sophie Partridge,
focus group participants

References

1   Dodd J, Sandell R, Delin A *et al. Buried in the footnotes*: *the representation of disabled people in museum and gallery coll ections*. Leicester: Research Centre for Museums and Galleries, 2004.

2   Family Resources Survey, 2008/9. www.officefordisability.gov.uk/research/facts-and-figures.php

3   Gleeson B. *Geographies of disability*. London: Routledge, 1999: chapter 5.

4   Davis LJ. *Enforcing normalcy: disability, deafness and the body*. London: Verso, 1995: 24.

5   Garland-Thomson R. Picturing people with disabilities: classical portraiture as reconstructive narrative. In: Sandell R *et al* (eds), *Re-presenting disability: activism and agency in the museum*. Abingdon: Routledge, 2010:24.

6   Buckland FT. A Chinese giant. In: *Leisure Hour*, No.728 (December 9, 1865):782–4.

7   Longmere PK. *Why I burned my book and other essays on disability*. Philadelphia: Temple University Press, 2003:131–48.

8   Garland-Thomson R. Picturing people with disabilities: classical portraiture as reconstructive narrative. In: Sandell R *et al* (eds), *Re-presenting disability: activism and agency in the museum*. Abingdon: Routledge, 2010:23.

9   Jordanova L. *Defining features: scientific and medical portraits 1660–2000*. London: Reaktion, 2000:14.

10 Huff JL. The dissemination, fragmentation and reinvention of the legend of Daniel Lambert, king of fat men. In: Tromp M (ed), *Victorian freaks*. Ohio: Ohio States University Press, 2008:40.

11 *Philosophical Transactions*, 1698.

12 Garland-Thomson R. *Extraordinary bodies: figuring physical disability in American culture and literature*. New York: Columbia University Press, 1997: photographs between 51–52.

13 *The Strand Magazine*, September 1894: 262.

14 Drimmer F. *Very special people: the struggles, loves and triumphs of human oddities*. New York: Bantam, 1976: 199.

15 Ibid: 200.

16 Mannix DP. *Freaks: we who are not as others*. New York: Juno Books,1999: 42.

17 Thompson CJS. *The mystery and lore of monsters*. London: Williams and Norgate, 1930: 175.

18 Howard M. *Victorian grotesque*. London: Jupiter Books, 1977: 23.

19 Thompson CJS. *The mystery and lore of monsters*. London: Williams and Norgate, 1930: 80.

20 Gama Machado J J. T*héorie des ressemblances, ou Essai philosophique sur les moyens de déterminer les dispositions physiques et morales des animaux, d'après les analogies de formes, de robes et de couleurs*. Paris: 1831–44.

21 Howard M. *Victorian grotesque*. London: Jupiter Books, 1977: 24.

22 Drimmer F. *Very special people: the struggles, loves and triumphs of human oddities*. New York: Bantam, 1976: 19.

23 Howard M. *Victorian grotesque*. London: Jupiter Books, 1977: 14.

24 Mannix DP. *Freaks: we who are not as others*. New York: Juno Books,1999: 61.

25 Harrison E. *The extraordinary case of Sarah Hawkes: one of extreme deformity cured by a method founded upon simple principles*. London: Joseph Robins, 1832: 6.

26 Ibid: 13.

27 Ibid

28 Ibid: 52.

29 Serny, J. *Spinal curvature: its consequences, and its cure*. London: 1840: 19.

30 Ibid

31 *The Lancet* 1834:3 May:207.

32 Gould GM, Pyle WL. *Anomalies and curiosities of medicine*. Philadelphia and London: WB Saunders, 1901: 907.

33 Jenner E. *An inquiry into the causes and effects of the variolae vaccinae, a disease discovered in some of the western countries of England,…and known by the name of the cow pox*. London, 179

34 Howard M. *Victorian grotesque*. London: Jupiter Books, 1977: 99.

35 Wellcome Library, London, Ephemera Collection: EPH4 99A.

36   *Portrait of Thomas Inglefield*, 1787. Etching by Thomas Inglefield after a drawing made by Charles Reuben Ryley. London, 1787. Wellcome Library no. 353i.

37   Ibid

38   Ibid

39   Pearson K, Nettleship E, Usher CH. *A monograph of albinism in man, part 1*. London: Dulau & Co, 1911: 234.

40   Royal College of Surgeons of England. *A visible difference: skin, race and identity, 1720–1820: an exhibition at the Royal College of Surgeons of England*, 2007. www.rcseng.ac.uk/museums/ exhibiting-difference/learning/resource_pack/Teachers % 20introduction % 20to % 20exhibition.pdf [accessed 11 August 2010].

41   Pearson K, Nettleship E, Usher CH. *A monograph of albinism in man, part 1*. London: Dulau & Co, 1911: 234.

42   Park K, Daston LJ. Unnatural conceptions: the study of monsters in sixteenth- and seventeenth-century France and England. *Past & Present*, 92 (Aug 1981):42–43

43   Mayo KB, Cropley TG. Jefferson, albinism, and vitiligo. *Archives of Dermatology* 2008 Nov; 144 (11): 1529.

44   Howard M. *Victorian grotesque: an illustrated excursion into medical curiosities, freaks and abnormalities, principally of the Victorian Age*. London: Jupiter Books, 1977: 48.

45   Martin CD. *The white African American body: a cultural and literary exploration*. Asbury Park, NJ: Rutgers University Press, 2002.

46   Hunter JC, Savin J. *Clinical dermatology*, 2nd edn. Oxford: Wiley Blackwell, 1994: 180–187

47   Royal College of Surgeons of England. *A visible difference: skin, race and identity, 1720–1820: an exhibition at the Royal College of Surgeons of England*, 2007. www.rcseng.ac.uk/museums/ exhibiting-difference/learning/resource_pack/Teachers % 20introduction % 20to % 20exhibition.pdf [accessed in August 2010].

48   Thompson CJS. *The mystery and lore of monsters*. London: Williams and Norgate, 1930: 199.

49   *Strand Magazine*, 1894: 259

50   Thompson CJS. *The mystery and lore of monsters*. London: Williams and Norgate, 1930: 199.

51   Ibid

52   Ibid

53   Ibid

54   Drimmer F. *Very special people: the struggles, loves and triumphs of human oddities*. New York: Bantam, 1976: 209.

55   Ibid: 198.

56   Caulfield J. *Portraits, memoirs and characters of remarkable persons*. London: Issac Herbert, 1819: 24.

57   Drimmer F. *Very special people: the struggles, loves and triumphs of human oddities*. New York: Bantam, 1976: 210.

58   Ibid: 211.

59   Gould GM, Pyle WL. *Anomalies and curiosities of medicine*. Philadelphia and London: WB Saunders 1901: 339.

60   Thompson CJS. *The mystery and lore of monsters*. London: Williams and Norgate, 1930: 227.

61   Ibid

62   Gould GM, Pyle WL. *Anomalies and curiosities of medicine*. Philadelphia and London: WB Saunders 1901: 339.

63   Drimmer F. *Very special people: the struggles, loves and triumphs of human oddities*. New York: Bantam, 1976: 30.

64   Howard M. *Victorian grotesque*. London: Jupiter Books, 1977: 31.

65   Thompson CJS. *The mystery and lore of monsters*. London: Williams and Norgate, 1930: 55.

66   Bondeson J. *The pig faced lady of Manchester Square and other medical marvels*. Stroud: Tempus, 2004: 10.

67   Ibid: 9.

68   Howard M. *Victorian grotesque*. London: Jupiter Books, 1977: 33.

69   Authentic account of a gigantic child. Letter to Joseph Planta, esq., secretary to the Royal Society, Enfield, Nov 25, 1779. *Gentleman's Magazine*, 50 (1780): Mar: 126–7.

70   Ibid

71   Ibid

72   Ibid

73   *Enfield, the environs of London: volume 2: County of Middlesex* (1795):278-334. www.british-history.ac.uk/report.aspx?compid=45413 [accessed 11 August 2010].

74   Caulfield J. *Portraits, memoirs and characters of remarkable persons from the revolution in 1688 to the end of the reign of George II. Collected from the most authentic accounts extant.* London: Young & TH Whitely, 1819–20: 103.

75   Ibid: 104.

76   Porter R. *Mind-forg'd manacles: a history of madness in England from the Restoration to the Regency.* London: Penguin Books, 1987: 122–123.

77   Caulfield J. *Portraits, memoirs and characters of remarkable persons from the revolution in 1688 to the end of the reign of George II. Collected from the most authentic accounts extant.* London: Young & TH Whitely, 1819–20: 103.

78   Caulfield J. *Portraits, memoirs and characters of remarkable persons.* London: Issac Herbert, 1794: 6.

79   *Philosophical Transactions*, 1698.

80   Caulfield J. *Portraits, memoirs and characters of remarkable persons.* London: Issac Herbert, 1794: 6.

81   *Philosophical Transactions*, 1698.

82   Caulfield J. *Portraits, memoirs and characters of remarkable persons.* London: Issac Herbert, 1794: 7.

83   Ibid: 6.

84   Khan J. *The heteradelph, or, double-bodied boy: introduced to the public at Dr Kahn's Museum, 4, Coventry Street, Leicester Square, London a lecture.* London: J Gilbert, *c*1865: 1.

85   Wellcome Library, London, Ephemera Collection EPH4 99A.

86   Caulfield J. *Portraits, memoirs and characters of remarkable persons.* London: Issac Herbert, 1819: 153

87   Ibid: 156.

88   Thompson CJS. *The mystery and lore of monsters.* London: Williams and Norgate, 1930: 58.

89   Bondeson J. *The pig faced lady of Manchester Square and other medical marvels.* Stroud: Tempus, 2004: 146.

90   Caulfield J. *Portraits, memoirs and characters of remarkable persons*. London: Issac Herbert, 1820: 37.

91   Thompson CJS. *The mystery and lore of monsters*. London: Williams and Norgate, 1930: 159.

92   Ibid: 56.

93   Caulfield J. *Portraits, memoirs and characters of remarkable persons*. London: Issac Herbert, 1819.

94   Ibid

95   Ibid

96   Ibid

97   Showhistory. www.showhistory.com

98   Thompson CJS. *The mystery and lore of monsters*. London: Williams and Norgate, 1930: 75.

99   Murdoch J. Gibson, Richard [Dwarf Gibson] (1605/1615?–1690). In: *Oxford dictionary of national biography*. Oxford: OUP, 2004; online edn, 2006. www.oxforddnb.com/view/article/10631 [accessed 1 April 2010].

100 Murdoch J, Murrell VJ. The monogramist DG: Dwarf Gibson and his patrons. *The Burlington Magazine*, Vol 123, No. 938 (May 1981): 282–91.

101 Murdoch J. Gibson, Richard [Dwarf Gibson] (1605/1615?–1690). In: *Oxford dictionary of national biography*. Oxford: OUP, 2004; online edn, 2006. www.oxforddnb.com/view/article/10631 [accessed 1 April 2010].

102 Disability Museum. www.disabilitymuseum.org

103 Kalter H. Origin and meaning of teratology. *Teratology*, vol. 65, 2002: 3–4.

104 Rollinus CJ. *Dissertatio anatomico-medica inauguralis duorum monstrorum anatomen et de causis monstrorum ulteriorem disquisitionem exhibens*. Gottingen: Abram Vandenhoeck, 1742.

105 Thompson CJS. *The mystery and lore of monsters*. London: Williams and Norgate, 1930: 72.

106 Davis LJ. *Enforcing normalcy: disability, deafness and the body*. London: Verso, 1995.

107 Sutherland A. *Disabled we stand*. Bloomington: Indiana University Press, 1984, c1981.